Miriam

ORLA
KELLY
PUBLISHING

by Adrian Wistreich

Orla Kelly Publishing,
27 Kilbrody, Mount Oval,
Rochestown Cork

For my friend David Dalton

Contents

CHAPTER 1

Marriage

We had been married for three years when Otto first slept with another woman. It wasn't until much later that he admitted it to me, during one of those bitter arguments about his behavior and my coolness toward him. He told me then that she was a younger friend of his father's mistress, whom he'd been introduced to on a short business trip, and he took advantage of the opportunity because he was sexually frustrated. He blamed me for his frustration because I had not allowed him to visit my bedroom since our eldest was born, who was now two. Otto claimed that he had felt nothing for the woman and put the night down to too much drink. He described his infidelity as 'necessary medicine for an ailment', and that as a result he had felt cured. He told me he had not felt guilty because I knew nothing about it, and he clearly persuaded himself that this was the only way to manage when I was just not interested in him on a personal level.

In the summer of 1918, when I was just twenty-one, my family and I had travelled to Pisztany, in Czechoslovakia, for six weeks at the spa. We were staying in the Thermia Palace, where all the royalty stayed, and I was with my uncle and aunt, who were also my guardians since my mother passed away when I was twelve. I can't recall where my brother was. He certainly wasn't with us that summer, but perhaps he was still away at boarding school, or at one of those sports camps he loved as a teenager. My older sister, Ania, must have been there, but I don't remember spending time with her, as she was already engaged to be married.

Uncle David stayed for a few days before returning to Krakow, but even while we were there, he spent his time with his network of business associates talking shop. Otto's father, Lolek Weiner was there, taking the waters and enjoying the spa with a younger woman I'd never seen before. She must have thought herself very exotic, but everyone else noticed how over-dressed and heavily made up she was. She had a husky voice from smoking Turkish tobacco. I didn't recognise her from Krakow, and avoided talking to her, but years later, Otto told me she was his father's mistress, Franzi. I'd met Lolek a few times before that summer, when he came to our home, and I hated his visits, because he was, frankly, far too familiar in his greetings. He stared at my décolletage when he bowed, insisted on kissing my hand at every opportunity, and regularly winked at me across the dinner table, while dropping double entendres. I couldn't say anything to my aunt about the offense he caused me, because Uncle David enjoyed his company and treated him with undue respect.

Lolek had recently brought Otto into Weiner's Tannery to work in his Krakow office, and was interested in taking shares in Papa and Uncle David's timber company if he could. After discussing a merger, during which he must have emphasised Otto's prospects for taking over the tannery, he and David arranged for Otto to be introduced to me at the regular hotel soiree. This was quite normal during the season, and the hotel ballroom was set out with a large number of tables around the dance floor with just this type of introduction in mind. Debutante balls were hugely popular in France and England, and the manager of the Thermia Palace tried to keep up with all the fashions.

At the soiree, David saw Otto wandering between the tables and called him over, making introductions to Aunt Jadzhia and me, and then we all had tea. Conversation was stilted, and even though Aunt Jadzhia spent some time telling Otto how accomplished I was at painting and drawing, in the kitchen and with my secretarial studies, she and David finally gave up trying to get him to talk directly to me. I remember being bored by him when we first met, and far more interested in the women around us, parading the latest fashions. He and David began to talk about business then, and I paid little attention to them until Otto stood and made his excuses. David and Jadzhia exchanged meaningful looks as he was taking his leave but said nothing. They seemed to be very keen on his meeting us all again, so despite his complete failure to engage me in conversation, and his lack of civility, Otto decided to ask if I might consider his calling on me the next day.

As expected of me, I had to accept his invitation, and we arranged to meet at 4pm in the conservatory, where Otto would reserve a table for tea. I arrived at the requisite time of 4.10pm, and Otto bowed. The sandwiches and cakes were already at the table, along with the silver tea service. Otto clearly didn't like to waste time.

"Your uncle is a very smart businessman, you know," he said. "We have worked closely together for some time, and my father and I are very impressed with his hardwood supply." As an opening remark, it was enough to make me lose concentration and to focus on the dancing. Otto was completely ill at ease with small talk and hadn't a notion of what would interest me.

"Do you live with David and his wife? I don't want to appear nosey, but are you orphaned?"

"No, my father is alive, but he is not in a position to take on parental duties as well as his work, so he has always looked to my uncle and aunt for support. Since my mother passed, I have been their ward. Papa is a sleeping partner in Uncle David's company. I am sure your father has met him at our house, on occasion."

I looked at him, trying to read his thoughts, and hoping to feel same spark, but he was staring at the tablecloth. I didn't find him in the least bit attractive. He was a short, square sort of man with a short neck and broad shoulders. He wore a moustache, which was supposed to be a handlebar, in the style of the Hussars, but hadn't reached maturity, and he wore spectacles. His eyes reminded me of the Mongolian or Russian races, and he had quite sallow skin. I thought then that his family might have originated from further east, but he didn't display the elegance of those races, and certainly didn't capture my imagination in a romantic or exotic way.

"Ah yes. I see…" Clearly his conversation topics had already evapourated. "And David tells me you've studied in secretarial college. Did you consider helping with in the timber company?" Perhaps he thought this was a modern thing to say, since it was quite unusual for young ladies to work in offices. He'd clearly been briefed about me by Uncle David. I had absolutely no interest in working in the family firm, and it was quite inappropriate that I was presented in this way to people, however modern it might sound. Why couldn't they present me as an individual in her own right?

"I have spent some time in his office, helping out when they are very busy, but my health prevents me from spending too long at the typewriter, and besides, I would prefer to be painting. People tell me I have quite a talent for the arts. I would have preferred to study at art school, you know, but my father thought otherwise."

Papa was not interested in what I wanted for myself. To him, women should be treated as chattels, to be traded in business, or as housekeepers to serve their elders. He would never agree to my artistic aspirations, and he just wanted to marry me off to an eligible man with prospects. I remember looking at Otto then and wondering whether David and Papa thought he was someone I should marry.

"I do so admire those with artistic leanings. It must have been hard for you to be directed towards office work if you wanted to be an artist." That raised my interest in Otto. I thought that there might yet be some hope for him, if that's what he thought, but in his next breath, he wiped away my hope that he could be different from other men.

"My mathematical mind doesn't draw me in that direction, but I am sure one needs an artist's eye for choosing one's wardrobe, or decor." So that was what he thought about creativity. That a woman should hone her artistic talents in order that she could help her husband with his interior design needs! Not satisfied with one faux pas, he just kept going.

"And do you have other hobbies? Do you like sewing or cooking? Do tell me what you enjoy most." He looked worried at the effect he was having on me with his attempts to understand me. His earnestness was amusing, in a way, though I tried not to show any pleasure in his company.

"Before my ski accident, my brother Paul and I used to go hiking, to Zakopane and in the Swiss Alps, but now I am plagued with sciatica and I spend many weeks each year taking the waters and having treatments," I replied.

People were moving towards the dance floor. The chamber orchestra had struck up mazurka, and everyone began to applaud. The music was delightful, and I really wanted to join the couples on the dance floor, though I couldn't imagine Otto being much of a dancer.

"I'm very interested in current affairs, and dancing, of course. Life can be so dull without parties, don't you think?" I thought it worth a try, to provoke him into some liveliness, by dropping hints to see if he would rise to the occasion.

"I'm afraid I'm not much of a dancer, Miriam," he said, staring again at the tablecloth, though he knew this was his cue. After another silence, he stood up, bowed, and took me for one carefully executed waltz before escorting me to the foyer so he could take his leave. The tea and cakes were untouched, and I knew I would be hungry long before dinner. We parted after no more than an hour, and without making any firm arrangement to meet again, which should have been message enough to Otto. Nevertheless, David and Jadzhia made sure we dined together within days, and they contrived other chance meetings in the week before Otto returned to Krakow.

When we returned from Pisztany, I thought I'd seen the back of him, but I was shocked to find that he had been invited to visit us by Uncle

David. That was when the penny dropped, and I realised that the family intended me to marry him. I kept out of the way as much as possible when he visited, though that seemed to make no difference, as nobody saw the need to bring me into their discussions. Such was the nature of arranged marriages. They were pre-determined by one's parents, or in my case by my guardians, without the input of one or sometimes either of the parties concerned. I do remember coming down to dinner after Otto had arrived and seeing him coming out of the study with my aunt. Uncle David called me in then and told me that Otto had asked for my hand that day, and that he had given the suit his blessing, subject, of course to my approval.

"I've spoken with your father, and we are very impressed with Otto. As you know, I've worked with his father, Lolek, for many years, and he is an astute man with a successful business. We feel that this is a good match. What do you say?"

I was panic stricken, and without the time to think, I felt ambushed.

"I'm sorry, Uncle David, but I don't have any feelings for Otto, and I don't think I would be happy with him. Please convey my apologies for his wasted trip."

"Now look here, Miriam. This is not the sort of offer that comes along every day. You're my ward, and your father agrees with me. "

Aunt Jadzhia had, along with my sister Ania, been my help-mate and protector and I turned to her to defend me against this attack. But she just stared at her hands and said nothing to endorse my refusal. She and David had already discussed the probability that I would demur.

"I'm sorry, Miriam, I have to agree that this is a good match. You'll do as you're told," she warned "You're in danger of being left on the shelf young lady."

I was a strong-willed girl, and while I loved my aunt, her exhortations were water off a duck's back to me. Unfortunately, Uncle David had another card to play:

"As I said, Miriam, your father approves this match, and if you refuse it, you will have to make your own way in the world. It's high time you were no longer dependent on us. I'll be happy to find you gainful employment as a governess or secretary elsewhere."

"I won't marry him!" I stormed out and spent the evening in my room, crying. Everyone knew better than to follow me, and they all left me to stew over the subject. I raged and cried, and felt bitter towards Ania for not helping me, but of course nobody changed their mind.

I've never been one to hold on to an inappropriate position in an argument, and when looked at coldly, I could see no sense in fighting. By the end of the evening, I'd changed my mind, and weighed up the prospect of Otto against the miserable life I saw myself having as a secretary in some grubby office and living in a rooming house for single women. I even began to agree with Jadzhia that I was in danger of becoming an old maid, even though I was just twenty-one at the time. David's practical nature and control of the allowance had had its effect. I could not imagine a world in which I would have to fend for myself financially and to manage on the meager income of a governess or secretary.

We were married in May 1919 and lived as man and wife for the next five years, during which time I had two children. Otto grew out of his bookish stuffiness and became a successful young businessman, and with my help, something of a socialite. The problem for Otto was, once I'd had the boys, I was no longer prepared to allow him into my room as often as he wanted. He had never been my choice, and I never enjoyed our relations. Our marriage was so much about our public relationship once the children had been born. That's not to say that I was unhappy. We worked well together, both socially, and in terms of our parenting responsibilities. Otto was very generous and didn't refuse me anything. I kept an excellent house, and our entertaining was renowned. The kitchen staff and maids were well trained and diligent, and Celestyna, our cook, was the talk of Krakow. Nevertheless, that was his excuse for straying.

By then he had moved out of Weiner and Sons workshops and into the offices of our family's firm, Blumenthal Hardwoods, as Papa had been forced to retire through ill health. He worked to develop the timber business by introducing modernisations, such as a telephone and proper double entry book keeping. He had a lot of ideas about expanding the timber export operations through his father's Danzig office, and also for combining the leather and timber businesses into a furniture operation. Rather than starting the furniture making from scratch, he and Lolek agreed to acquire an interest in an existing company, called Ostapowicz and Son. Through this merger, Otto began working with a business partner, several years his senior. Olek Ostapowicz was a war veteran and a quiet, thoughtful man. He was warm and generous, as well as a steady hand in the business. As soon as Otto invited Olek and his wife Maryla to dinner, I took to them both. He had married shortly after the war, at the age of thirty-three, and she was then only nineteen. When we met she was still in her early twenties and I felt quite maternal towards her. We quickly became friends, and she looked to me for advice and support. She was intelligent and energetic, though far less independent in nature than me. She was quite innocent, and she had clearly never had any boyfriends before being introduced to Olek. She wanted much personal advice and was fascinated by motherhood and all its responsibilities.

We spent a lot of time together in those years after the boys were born, and often made up a foursome for trips out on Olek's yacht or for picnics in the country. I saw how Otto watched Maryla, when we were all together and I wondered what he thought of her. She was clearly in love with Olek, who was devoted to her, and protected her as a father might his daughter, and she didn't seem to notice Otto's attentions.

CHAPTER 2

Vichy

I planned to stay for a few weeks in Vichy over the summer, with my youngest, Anna, to take the waters as much as to get away from the heat of Krakow. It wasn't her first visit, and as she was already twelve, it would be an excellent opportunity for her to improve her French. I could catch up with the Epsteins and the Steinbergs, who stay at the Hershey for a month every July. Stashek has some financial interest in the hotel I think, as he is so well treated there, but in any case, they always take the same suites on the first floor, the ones with the balconies overlooking the pine forest.

Otto and I had a couple of weeks in The Hershey with Olek and Maryla in thirty-three, or thirty-four, I forget which. Otto was distracted and disinterested in the company, and it would have been a miserable trip, but I found the treatments did me a power of good. He and I were regular guests there in the twenties when the boys were younger, but that was when we used to travel as a family, when Otto and I enjoyed each other's company, at least sometimes. But in the last few seasons, I have taken to visiting alone, or with Anna alone for company. I find that the various mud bath and sulphur treatments help with my rheumatism and sciatica, which I have suffered with ever since my ski accident all those years ago. Having children of course exacerbated it, especially as Tomasz was a massive four kilos. It's such a shame that I can no longer ski, since the winter travel is quite limited in Europe, and Zakopane is so beautiful in the snow. I do miss the resort every February, but of course there's no point being stuck there in the Palace Hotel with nothing to do but sit in one's furs by the lake and watch the skaters having their fun. What parties we had as teenagers!

Paul was always an excellent skier, starting as all the Polish men do, at two or three years of age. And he is a fearless climber. Last year he climbed the Matterhorn, and he took his small Leica camera, the one which Otto and I had given him for his twenty-first, so he could give me a photograph of himself at the summit. He's a couple of years younger than I, but for as long as I can remember he has been a stronger skier than me. When I had my fall, he literally carried me on his back while skiing down to the village. I was in agony, all the way down, but I felt quite safe. He competed in several races that year too, and he has a number of trophies. Paul is highly regarded for his work as a senior civil engineer in the city council in Krakow, and from what people tell me, he will take over the planning department's management of roads soon.

Before the family started visiting Vichy, we always spent our summers in Naleczow, near Lublin, since it is only a few hours' drive from Krakow. It's a charming Polish spa town with quaint streets and good dining. When Otto and I married, we went there a few times, rather than travelling overseas, because he preferred to be close to the office. I always found it to be an excellent spa and a top-quality hotel, where we were friends with the Maitre D, and were well treated. But from what Ania tells me, one couldn't be sure that they could provide the service now. She continues to stay there, but she told me that last year they were already short-staffed, and that many of the friends we used to meet there had either stopped taking the waters or were already staying on the French Riviera or Capri. Poland really has come under severe pressure economically it seems. Otto knows so much more about it than I do, though I do try to keep up with the news. I know it isn't considered appropriate for a woman to follow politics, or read the business pages, but I'm not interested in being a wallflower. Sometimes I wish Otto would be more open over his concerns about the business and the economy. I have to find out what I can over the dinner table by asking Olek and the other businessmen who are more prepared to open up about their affairs. All the talk of war, and the way that the National Socialists in Germany are behaving, has begun to undermine confidence among Polish exporters, though some see Hitler's ambitions as an opportunity to sell their goods. All in all, whatever is going on in Germany, it is depressing the Polish way of life, and I just couldn't face another summer of Otto in Naleczow, and all the provincial conversation.

So this year, Vichy seemed the best idea, because the boys are both in London, studying, and I have arranged for Anna and me to travel to Paris to meet them there, before their autumn term begins, for a few days and to reassure myself that Max is getting down to his studies. He's only been there for a year, and while Tomasz is a responsible older brother, and is looking after him in the evenings, he is too busy with his own university studies to pay adequate attention to Max's attendance at school.

The weather in Vichy has been fine and dry. The drive from the station was glorious, since Monsieur Beranger, the General Manager, kindly sent the open topped Citroen to collect us. The chauffeur was resplendent in his uniform, and the sun shone through the plain trees which line the whole route and which are so characteristic of France. The Hotel Hershey doesn't seem to have suffered the privations, which we've seen in Poland. When its copper green roof and the quaint tower came into view, I felt quite sentimental. There have been so many years when we enjoyed our summer here. The car swept around to the front entrance, with the portico and staircase in all its splendour, and the chauffeur called two bellboys to take the trunks, as Monsieur Beranger himself came to greet us at the door. The lobby is just as opulent and accommodating as always, and I was delighted that we have been given our favourite room, on the second floor. Once we'd settled ourselves and discussed unpacking with the maid, we took a tour of the ballroom, where the hotel was serving afternoon tea, accompanied by a string quartet in full evening dress. It is just as splendid as I remember it, full of fashion and bustle. And still the same faces. Our waiter, Hugo, was effusive. I know he is trained to be so, and of course we always give him a large tip when we leave, but I do think he is fond of us. He always remembers Anna's name, and often takes her into the kitchens to say hello to the chef. Hugo has been here forever, like most of the staff. He brought us the most delicate patisserie with our tea today.

Their wonderful Sicilian marzapane and caliscioni, the macaroons and puff pastry flutes filled with almond paste are renowned, and I have to ration myself, and Anna, every time we come. The Parisians are here in force of course, talking at the tops of their voices and looking down their noses at me when they realise I'm from the East, despite my excellent French, which is quite tiresome.

But there are still friends from Vienna here. I met the Weinreichs and Deiter Koch having their tea in the hotel today. They have apparently taken the summer house which they often rent for the season, which comes with an open invitation to use the Hershey's facilities. Eleanor told me that they had to get away from Vienna, because of the military. It seems that there were soldiers everywhere, and one couldn't get served in any of the best restaurants, which were over-run with Nazi officers. We have even seen one or two uniforms since we've been here. They're French soldiers, of course, but so far the place has an air of calm the like of which I haven't felt for some time. I must say I mused about trying to persuade Otto to look for a property here which we could stay longer in. He could transact business in Danzig and Anna could spend a year in a lycee Francais. I resolved to look for somewhere while we're here.

Last week Anna had her birthday tea party at the hotel. I allowed her to invite some young Vichissois girls she'd befriended, and they managed to behave like young ladies, dressed to the nines as they were, in brightly coloured summer frocks and lace bonnets. Anna is still very childlike, but one of two of the French girls were the shape of young adults, and needless to say, attracted the attention of every teenage boy in the room, not to mention their fathers. I do find French men a little sleazy. It's not that I don't like to be noticed. Of course I do, and I am. I'm considered younger than my years and was always a head turner. It's just that the French tend to touch one at any opportunity, and the conversation is littered with double entendres, which of course is a French expression, because they seem to have invented the game. They always bring to mind Otto's insufferable father, Lolek.

Anna is doing well with her French, talking with Hugo and enjoying the company of the French children. She was never a boisterous child, but I must say how pleased I am to see her coming out of herself this year for the first time. I think of this summer as perhaps the last of her childhood. From next year, I will have to start teaching her the ways of a young lady, which of course will be a pleasure of its own.

CHAPTER 3

Paris

Anna and I took the train to Paris three days ago, having bade farewell to our friends who remain, and to M. Beranger. Vichy never changes, which is its greatest achievement. I wondered, as we drove to the station, how it would be affected, should a war ensue. It's hard to imagine soldiers encamped on the lawns of The Hershey, or suave officers dancing in the ballroom in their French uniforms.

We had couchettes on the sleeper, which was fun for Anna, though the sheets weren't what I'd call pristine, and our guard was rushed off his feet, because the first-class compartments were full. Half of Paris seemed to be returning from Vichy, and all the talk was of war. August had been sweltering and Paris would have been unbearable, so I'm glad we left it till the end of the month to travel. Tomasz and Max have to be back in London for the start of term in two weeks' time. Otto had agreed to our meeting on the basis of my proposal to quiz Max on his studies and had wired the money for their travel to Tomasz in July.

We arranged to meet the boys at the hotel, since they had been travelling for much longer than us and would need to rest. I booked us two rooms at the Georges Cinq, which was an extravagant treat for Tomasz, whom I know has been living in some dank basement in Bloomsbury, in London, during the last year. We discussed his finding better digs, but Otto wasn't prepared to fund luxuries of any sort, and Tom, typically disinterested in his material wellbeing, hasn't complained once about his allowance. He has even been looking for a job in London to supplement his income.

He and Max came from London via Dover, by train and ferry, which took the best part of 24 hours, because apparently the railways in Britain are full of troops and the ferry timetable was disrupted. Tomasz is a good sailor, while Max clearly spent the voyage leaning over the rail and vomiting. But Max loves his food and had already recovered by the time their train reached the Gard Du Nord.

Tomasz looked thinner, I thought, though as handsome as ever. Max must have been shaving since he left home, and his face was pockmarked and spotty. The poor boy always had the tendency to run to fat, which wasn't helped by his greed as a child. He used to steal my chocolate, which I had to secure under lock and key, and he became quite obese, though he does seem to have shaken that off a little. It's five months since I last saw him, and he's shot up several inches in height and his trousers are already too short, though they were only purchased in July.

Tomasz is in his second year at University College London, which is one of the best academic institutions in Europe for scientists, I am told. He is such a bright boy, and he's studying Metallurgy and Physics for his Bachelor of Science Degree. He chose the subjects, which I must say sound extremely complicated, because he loves numbers and is fascinated by how machines work. It is hard to know where the studies will lead, but he is so brilliant, there is no doubt he will become successful in whatever he does. I should think he wants to become a famous scientist. I supported his plans, while Otto would have had him study business at Krakow University, or even miss his studies to go straight into the firm, so he could at some point take over the timber business. It seemed ridiculous to me that Otto, who is not yet fifty, would want to line Tomasz up as his successor now, when he may not retire for ten years or more. I knew that this wasn't what Tomasz wanted, and besides, Max is younger and much more suited, and still has time to grow into that role. Tomasz is far too academic and not at all interested in money, while Max has always been the negotiator, trading with his pals at school, buying and selling his way around the neighbourhood. He'll make a fine businessman, I think. In many ways, he is quite like Lolek, his grandfather, though hopefully not such a roué! Tomasz, on the other hand, takes after Ada, his grandmother. Lolek ran the best-known tannery and belt factory near Krakow, and Otto has taken over that business and merged it into my family's timber business, which he now runs with Olek. Ada, God rest her, was the youngest of five girls, and she went to university in Vienna to study Chemistry, which was very unusual for a woman, especially before the Great War. I greatly admired her, and I too should have had such an opportunity. Ada was interested in the chemistry of tanning, which is why her family funded her studies. She must have had a lot to put up with in her marriage to Lolek, who was much more interested in skirt than business. He was like a limpet towards me, before Otto and I were married and even when I was pregnant. Many's the time I was forced to slap his hands away from my bodice. If he hadn't been so charming, I would have been much more brusque with him, but he always managed to smooth-talk his way out of embarrassment when he'd gone too far. I often wonder how he begat Otto.

I remember that even when I first knew him, in his late fifties, Lolek loved to socialise, and spent a good deal of time out on the town, in Krakow. According to Otto, he was always womanizing and drinking, and had even dragged Otto into some of his trips, ostensibly for business. Not that any of that rubbed off on Otto as far as I can tell. He hasn't enough charm, let alone too much!

Ada, on the other hand, was a quiet academic, and while Lolek was away gallivanting, she stayed at home with her books, and helped to educate Otto and his brother, which is why Otto became so interested in his studies. She knew what Lolek was like but in the same way as my family pushed me towards Otto, she understood how important the match was for her family and did not expect marriage to be about love either.

When I was seventeen, I wanted nothing more than to fall in love, and to marry for love, and to live happily ever after, but once I'd had my first love taken from me, I realized that it is just too painful to live in that way, and that it's more important to have companionship, respect and honesty in a marriage. When it came to Otto, I suppose I started out with those expectations, but lost all three. As for the romance, I didn't have even that to fall back on.

One has to question whether arranged marriages are in the end more successful than marriages for love. But there is no point, in my view, questioning for long something one can't change. It will of course be interesting when Tomasz' time comes, or Anna's, to see what freedoms they are given by Otto. For myself, I think I would prefer that they choose a partner for life whom they are at least attracted towards, though I suppose, looking back, that Josef and I might have suffered too much hardship for our love to blossom. We would have been cut off in the world, coming as we did from two such different cultures. But what's the point of speculation. I have to stop myself daydreaming that one day I'll be in Vienna, walking down the Ringstrasse, towards the Opera, and will see Josef walking towards me, though in my daydreams he often has a young wife on his arm.

Otto agreed to Tomasz studying in London, after a little persuasion by me. He was more resistant to sending Max to Britain two years later, though, and he only agreed to that provided Max was under Otto's control and protection. Max is to matriculate in two years' time, and when he returns to Krakow, he is immediately to be apprenticed in the office. Max moved to London last year, when he turned sixteen, and he has lodged with Tom in his digs, since apparently the landlady is quite kind and cooks for them. Max is supposed to be studying hard, with Tom's guidance. He is something of a lazy boy, and Otto and I feel that he might pull his socks up under Tom's influence. I'm not sure just how much he listens to Tom, and whether he can be kept from roaming the London streets looking for adventure, but at least he'll be in a centre of learning, and without the distractions he's come to know in Krakow. He failed several examinations at school and was absent without leave on several occasions. He was never particularly troublesome at home, and usually came home in time to eat, but he often seemed to have money, which hadn't been given to him, and I'm sure he wasn't working for it.

When we reached the hotel, the Maitre D told me that the boys had arrived, and that lunch had been sent up to their room. As soon as we had been taken up to our own room, I went straight to the connecting door and opened it without warning, to find Max sprawled on the bed, full clothed and surrounded by dirty plates. He was asleep. Tomasz was in the bath.

"Well that's a fine sight! Max, for goodness sake get your dirty boots off the bedspread. If you are so tired, then have a bath and go to bed for the afternoon. And before you do so, put those plates onto the trolley and ring for someone to collect them. Oh, Tomasz, how well you look. You really should eat more, though, I can see your ribs."

"Mamushu." Tom kissed me on both cheeks in a very mature gesture. "How was your journey?" He looked splendid with a towel around his waist, in the bathroom doorway, grinning. "And Anna, how's my favourite sister?"

"I'm your only sister, Tom. How can I be your favourite?"

CHAPTER 4

Maryla

We spent a few precious days together, as planned, touring museums and galleries, walking in the Tuileries and strolling on the banks of the Seine. The boys were full of stories about their year together in London, and what they had been getting up to in their spare time. Other than one or two military parades in the Champs Elysees, there was no evidence of soldiers, though there was clearly a lot of tension. While we were there, some newspapers, which had run articles in praise of Hitler's pact with Stalin, were confiscated from the newsstands, and there was talk of evacuating children from the city if war was declared. Though we avoided listening to French radio stations, or buying Le Monde, it was pretty clear that the Parisians thought war was imminent. We decided to act like tourists, and to do our best to ignore all the signs.

It was an idyllic few days spent in a beautiful city in the late summer sun, and looking back on them, they were really the last time all four of us felt like a happy family. It's easy in retrospect to recognise the pleasure in something one takes for granted at the time. It is harder to see the good in something, which at the time seems awful.

I didn't want to know what Germany proposed to do in Poland, even though it was becoming inevitable that they would declare war. Britain's prime minister, Neville Chamberlain, gave his assurance that he would bring his army to the defense of Poland, and on that basis, we had to assume that everyone and everything we held dear in Krakow would be safe. My spoken French is excellent, while my reading is a little rusty, so even if I had bought Le Monde, I would not perhaps have understood the nuances of Hitler's negotiations with Britain and France, or how he had been playing a double game with Russia, or just how close we were coming to war.

It had been a good summer vacation until then. To be honest, I was glad to be away on my own. Otto had been impossible to talk to for months, and I was heartily sick of hearing his excuses for not being at home. He was happy to lie without compunction about business trips and late nights in the office, and I knew full well that he was spending as much time as he could with Maryla Ostapowicz. Of course he denied it, which was frankly demeaning, as it was pretty common knowledge among our set in Krakow that they were having an affair. If I hadn't worked out what was going on myself months ago, there were plenty of busybodies ready to give me sympathetic looks and mutter behind their hands about it. Otto is such a disingenuous man in many ways, and not at all sophisticated in his deceptions.

Why he chose to have an affair with Maryla, the wife of his business partner, when we've all known each other half our lives is beyond me. Olek has been Otto's close friend and trusted partner in the furniture business for years, for goodness sake, and I've minded her children and she mine, and Anna and Aneta go to the same school too. I wonder how long it has been going on.

I should be outraged by their behaviour. I'm sure Olek would be if he knew. But then, how could he not know, unless he is burying his head in the sand because he and Maryla's sex life has, according to her, stopped. Perhaps he does, and hasn't the strength to do anything about it, especially if he's not sleeping with her. She told me that they had wanted children so much, and that they were having great difficulties conceiving. Then Szymon and Aneta were born, and Maryla inferred that their visits to the fertility specialist I recommended had worked wonders. I thought it strange at the time that they were hardly enjoying a healthy relationship in the bedroom, but perhaps they injected some effort into their marriage because the doctor gave them hope. But who knows what goes on behind closed doors in a marriage. Look at mine, after all. Everyone saw us as the perfect couple in love, and then when the stories began to circulate, and I saw the looks they all gave me…

I've always had a soft spot for Olek, and even though he is a charming and attractive man, I am sure that I wouldn't consider cheating on Otto with him. I'm not saying that I have not been attracted to other men since Otto and I were married, but really, our closest friends and his business partner? It is outrageous! I would like to think of myself as a good wife. I have always tried to be dutiful and kind. I look on Olek as a father figure, and he certainly has been a gentle influence in Max's life, which makes a change from Otto's heavy-handed approach to parenting. I sometimes wish that Olek had been Max's father.

When I try to understand the attraction between Otto and Maryla, I am dragged down to assuming it has nothing to do with emotion, and everything to do with lust. They are like chalk and cheese on all other levels, after all. It is fair to say that Maryla is a kind and quiet young woman. She is beautiful too in her way. I ought to feel jealous and to hate her for sleeping with my husband, but in all truth, I don't want to stand in their way, if it keeps the peace and allows me to have my own privacy without Otto intruding. Last time we were intimate together, in June I think, he came to my room late at night, after being out for dinner, and smelling of alcohol and cigars. I would have locked the door but had assumed he would be too drunk to bother me. Instead, he made no pretense of wanting to woo me or give me any pleasure. It was no more than a mounting, in which he did what he'd come to do and then left. I felt dirty and hurt and have diligently locked my door ever since.

Perhaps Maryla was too young for Olek. I gather that their marriage was arranged, and although Olek was already doing well in his work, and was certainly a good catch, it isn't fair to a woman who is still in her teens, and in her first flush of adulthood, to be tied to a much older man. They were having great difficulty starting a family, and in the first years of their marriage, I was something of a confidante to Maryla, though it was not something I relished. She did explain to me, with a great deal of embarrassment, that Olek had received mercury treatment for a venereal disease some years before they met, which he contracted during the Great War, as so many soldiers did. I must say when I heard that story, I assumed he might be unable to produce any children, though I didn't tell Maryla my view. We were all surprised when she became pregnant with Szymon, and then only eighteen months later, with Aneta. They are lovely children, so well behaved. Szymon has a sharp mind too, like Tomasz, and they always enjoyed talking together when they were younger, even though he's several years younger than Tom. Once I overhead them talking about mathematical theories together, like two research scientists.

I didn't see it coming, the affair between Otto and Maryla, but in hindsight, I can see why he pursued her. He and I have never been close in that way, and yet he has a powerful drive when it comes to the bedroom. I was never attracted by that side of him, and I think I only agreed to marry him out of the desperation I felt to escape my fate after my father refused the suit of Josef. Josef was my first love, but he was a Turk, and as such, completely unacceptable to my family, even though he was a doctor. I met him, and fell in love with him, at the age of eighteen. It was just after the Great War, while I was visiting Vienna, and I would have gladly married him if Papa had not considered him beneath the family's dignity. I remember overhearing Uncle David agreeing: "It would not do for her to marry a Turk." Then I was summoned to my father and told in no uncertain terms that my liaison must cease immediately. I was very angry, and refused to stop seeing him, so Aunt Jadzhia was enlisted to take me to Berlin for a week, against my will, and when I returned I tried to contact Josef without success. I wrote so many letters to him but received no replies. I assumed that in my absence, my father and Uncle David had demanded that he leave me alone. I thought that Josef, who loved me with all his heart, would find a way around them to contact me and that we would make secret assignations. But I heard nothing at all. It was the cruelest fate for a teenage girl in love.

It transpired that once they had demanded Josef's word that he would not try to see me again, Ania did as she was told and blocked all his letters from reaching me. I only found that out years later, and I have always found it hard to forgive her for that. I was expecting to be sent to Geneva to a finishing school, but as some sort of punishment for my innocent affair, Papa decided that I should not be allowed to go and instead would be put to work in the family firm as a secretary. For months, I had been scared that I would be sent away so that I would have no chance of seeing Josef, but once he had been banished from my life, I began to wish I were going to Switzerland. If that wasn't going to happen, I would have liked to go to an art school and perhaps become an artist but was instead forced to enter the local secretarial college and study shorthand and typing. It was a terrible come down, and I felt demeaned. Many of my school friends were engaged to be married, and I was being sent out to learn to be an office worker!

Not that I rebelled. In fact, I matriculated with high honours as the top student in the class and spent many tedious hours each day in my father's office that winter. It was at that time that he agreed with David that I needed some sort of maternal influence in my life, and as he was always so busy at work, that I and Paul should move in with them. I thought it unnecessary, and I knew that Aunt Jadzhia, whom I always saw as rather dull, would provide nothing more than a curb on my social life. Paul, on the other hand was still at school, and he looked up to Uncle David, who certainly spent a lot more time with him than Papa had. Also, David and Jadzhia lived outside Krakow in a large house, with grounds, and stables. They had horses and both Paul and I loved to ride, so we both accepted the move without complaint. Ania was already engaged to Isidor, a suave young businessman with political aspirations, and she continued to live with Papa, though she was more of a housekeeper than I would have chosen to be.

That year when David and Jadzhia took me to Pisztany, and I was introduced to Otto, I couldn't imagine him being in any way suitable. He was certainly interested in me, in his way, but I was still heartbroken over Josef, and of course I refused to consider anyone else. Even then, in the beginning, he seemed to me to be like a block of wood. I may have been a petulant young woman, but he made little effort to please me, even though he was obviously being encouraged to court me. I often wonder what would have happened to my life had my father agreed to my marrying Josef. I might be living in Istanbul now.

CHAPTER 5

Leaving Paris

After our week in Paris, I planned that we would all travel on to London together and Anna and I would stay at a small private hotel in Holburn, near Tomasz and Max, for the autumn, rather than returning to Krakow. I came up with this plan only days before we left Vichy for Paris, because the newspapers were full of stories about the German army mobilising, and the failure of our Government to engage in planning the country's defense. Even in my inexperienced view, Germany might decide at any time to attack us in Krakow. All the talk in Vichy had been of war, and I felt it would be better to be close to the children, in the relative safety of London, rather than being divided at this time.

I made this decision alone, but whatever I felt about Otto's behaviour, he was still my husband and on some level I still felt beholden to him. I felt obliged to check my plans with him first, against my intuitive judgment. Otto had told me he would be in Danzig on business throughout the second half of August, though I assumed it was because Maryla was there. In fact, she was at home, and he really was at the Danzig office. I telegraphed him with my proposal to go to London and was somewhat taken aback by his terse response insisting that Anna and I return to Krakow immediately, leaving Tomasz and Max to travel back to England without us.

'Pack up the apartment and take Ania's family with you to Naleczow where you will be safe. You must not remain in France. You must return home.'

I was furious at his lack of consideration for my wishes, and his disregard for our safety. Why would it be better to be in Poland, when Germany had been focused on the East, and not in Britain, with the English Channel between the children and Hitler? I would so much have liked to telephone him and have a sensible discussion about our plan, but it would have been impossible to get through in the circumstances. Hitler had introduced a ban on international telephone calls for all those based in Germany and of course Danzig was within this remit. Besides, I was sure I couldn't have presented our case in a cool and calm way even if I had been able to reach Otto. It was not simply the issue of safety, though that was paramount. It was the lack of independent choice I was expected to accept. Otto's interest in the children's welfare was hardly apparent at the best of times, and I had made all important decisions about their upbringing, which by and large he had gone along with. Now I was making decisions for their safety, and he was blocking them. Perhaps he had access to privileged information on what was going to happen in Europe, but I doubted he had any better idea than anyone else. Isidor might have been the one person in the family to give me good advice but getting Isidor to contact Otto on my behalf was not practical.

Looking back, I think Otto's first concern must have been to bring as many of his family together in our home country as possible, but at the time I got his reply, I could only see selfishness in his demands. He probably wanted the apartment to be taken care of, and I was sure he was worried because he was parted from Maryla, though of course he wouldn't say that, since he hadn't admitted to their relationship.

When I met Olek, a few days later, it transpired that Otto was unable to return immediately from Danzig due to some problems with his travel papers, which he could have told me about in the telegraph. I only found out after Anna and I had begun our return journey that he was effectively leaving us alone in Poland while remaining in The Free State. Before we booked our train tickets, I did really consider ignoring his telegraph, pretending even that it had not been delivered to the Georges Cinq. But I am fundamentally honest, and loyal, and I couldn't bring myself to go against so firm a demand while staying married to him. I felt obliged to go along with his decision, and it was with reluctance that I made plans to travel from Paris to Krakow via Berlin, on the Nord Express.

After I had booked the train I received another telegram from Danzig.

'I have decided to join my old regiment if possible and I leave for Rumania in the morning.'

That really added insult to injury! How could he demand my return to Poland only to absent himself with this hair-brained scheme to enlist? Whatever his view of my independence and capability in a crisis, he was responsible for our family and owed nothing to his regiment. We Jews must stick together. We are being assaulted with hatred. The regime in Germany is poisonous and it is shocking to see Hitler's propaganda gaining momentum and support, even in other countries. Yes, we are Poles and proud of our nationality, but we are a family, and a race under threat, and we have to look after our own.

Besides, Otto is already in his mid-forties, and could not possibly be any use to his regiment. His place is at home, looking after the business in Krakow, not fighting a cause, which he's shown little interest in before. It is over twenty years since he had anything to do with the Polish army, and from what little I know, they are not a strong defense against the might of Hitler. He'll be killed as soon as he is on the battlefield! But I know that there is no reasoning with Otto when he has the bit between his teeth. He is clearly unhappy with my freedom while taking advantage of his own, without consultation. And where is Maryla in all this? I find it strange that he would leave her behind. I must approach Olek carefully to find out what he thinks of the plan.

After the second telegram, in my anger, I considered again ignoring Otto and travelling to London with the boys. I would have done so had he been on his way back to Krakow, because I could rely on him then to take care of the family in Poland, but now that he was planning on travelling to Rumania, and was clearly not prepared to take responsibility for his own in Poland, I knew that I must return in order to find Ania and Paul at home, if they have not already moved to the country. It is so hard here in Paris to establish just how worried everyone is at home, but from what news I can glean, Hitler's intentions are to invade Poland, and that Stalin intends to defend the nation against the Nazis. The expectations of a German invasion, in the articles I read in Le Monde, are very disconcerting, and if they are true, Hitler's forces will reach Krakow quickly from the eastern border. It is not clear what interest Russia has in Poland, since to my knowledge they have never been particularly warm to us. I surmise that they would like to occupy the country in order to milk us for our resources, which they badly need. This is not so much a defense of Poland by Stalin as another invasion from the East.

If Poland is facing two threats, with the Germans invading from the west and the Russians from the East, the Krakow Army is not going to be in a position to defend us against either advance, and the Carpathian Army, which has been defending our Eastern borders for months, is not going to get back quickly to help, if, that is, they dare to leave the border open to the massive Russian armies. I feel that by returning I will be putting my head between the jaws of a fierce lion, like some circus performer.

According to this morning's papers, the Germans and Russians have signed a pact in Moscow, not to fight one another. It surprised everyone, because we thought the Germans hated the Slavs, and didn't their last agreement fall apart? And I must say that I understood Stalin was talking about a pact with France, which the newspapers were very positive about when we were in Vichy. It all feels so confusing that I am unable to look far enough ahead to make a decision. I feel that we just have to get on with our lives and leave these posturing madmen to decide what they want.

We seem now to be dependent on our agreement with Britain and France to protect us, but I don't understand how they could possibly reach Poland quickly without aeroplanes. It is a hollow pact, especially with Germany in between us and them, to agree to help us defend ourselves from both these powerful enemies. And what will happen to the people living in the middle?

It has not been easy to focus on the children these last few days, and on the beautiful art we have been seeing, when I fear that returning to

Krakow will put us in the greatest danger. I have been tempted to discuss it with Tomasz, because he is a sensible young man, despite his mere nineteen years, but I see that he only hopes we will come to London and doesn't understand why Otto would demand our return to Poland. In his world, Otto is an unreasonable bully, so it's not possible to have a rational discussion with him about this.

We visited the Grande Synagogue de la Victoire today. I had never been inside and since it is the home of the Chief Rabbi of Paris, I thought we should take a look. I decided that even though I have never held strong beliefs and have really only played the part of being a Jewess, I should encourage the children more. Certainly, David and Jadzhia brought me up correctly. Papa also made sure that I became a Bat Mitzvah when I was thirteen, and we attended the synagogue on High Holy Days and for ceremonies. But since Otto and I have not seen much of one another since the spring, the subject of a Bat Mitzvah ceremony for Anna has not been discussed. We have not been near a synagogue in Krakow since Max's Bar Mitzvah, and that was a happier time when we were all together. Max asked only yesterday about visiting the Grande Synagogue, and about Anna's Bat Mitzvah and teased her about learning the Torah. I said that we would go and see the rabbi when we return to Krakow, though even if he is able to offer us a date, I doubt we can get enough people together for a minyan just now. Perhaps it will have to wait until things calm down. Maybe in the spring.

La Victoire was truly splendid, and well worth the visit. Its huge portico and massive interior left us all silent. Then Anna picked up a guide and was quoting statistics at me for the whole time we were inside.

"Mamushu, did you know that it can seat 1800 people? It was built in 1867 by the Rothschild family. Aren't they the wealthiest Jews in the world? Look at the stained-glass windows, Max. Twelve windows for the twelve tribes."

By the time she had read out all the facts, my mind was drifting back to my own Bat Mitzvah and the beautiful dress which Jadzhia had bought for me. I was trying to recall whether my father was at the party, but I can't see him in my mind's eye. I'm no longer sure if he was there. My memory of him is vague, and I have never really asked myself, or others who could have told me, the questions a daughter would want to answer: Why did he pass the responsibility for my upbringing to Uncle David and Aunt Jadzhia once my mother died? Why didn't he keep in close touch, even if he felt unable to manage the children? Did he love us? Did he have any interest in re-marrying after mother passed? I must talk to Ania about that when I next meet her.

We sat for some time in the pews, staring up at the amazing domed ceiling in the choir. There is a power, which emanates from the architecture. It seems to hold a strength in its fabric which gives us hope for an end to all the terrible things which are happening. Max wanted to know about why the Nazis hate the Jews, and I would like to have had a good answer for him, but I didn't. I wanted to ask someone else to explain it all to the children. I wanted desperately to be able to ask someone to take this weight from me and to be strong for me. Otto, why did you desert me now? What happened that has left me here, trying to answer Max, worrying for Anna, holding my head up for Tom?

I told the children that it wasn't really caused by something that happened, but that Hitler wanted someone to blame for everything that had gone wrong in Germany when they lost the Great War. Some people thought he was a Jew himself, but he'd written a book that railed against the Jews, which I had seen in all the bookshops in Vienna, and which was like some new bible in Germany apparently.

We sat for a few more moments in the nave, before we got up to leave. I had a sense of peace I haven't felt since Vichy, and I think I could have stayed there a long time. There were several people praying, and I very much wanted to have the strength of faith to join them, but I can't find it in me. I wanted to find Rabbi Hertzog to ask him what we should do. Of course that was impossible, and besides, what could he possibly say about the future. I knew it wasn't the place of a Rabbi to answer these impossible questions, but I wanted someone independent and astute to assess our plans. I had never felt so alone, or so responsible as I did in that place. I realised in that moment that I do not believe in God. I don't believe that some higher being is controlling our destiny. I don't believe that the terrible world in which we live can be under the protection of an all-powerful God unless he plans to punish humanity, and I don't want to believe that. I don't think I am prepared any more to guide Anna into something that I do not believe in. I don't see that I have a right to choose for her, and she will, I am sure, make her own decision on her own faith once she's older. But for now, it isn't possible anyway, so there is no need to decide. Besides, everyone goes through these ceremonies, and few of us are good Jews. It is hard to hold a faith in such turbulent times, though of course many believers would argue that this is the one time to hold together and to pray together. Coming to some sort of conclusion in that place was a relief. I felt immediately lighter, as though I had taken off a rain-soaked cloak. But I also felt cold and exposed. If this is what self-reliance feels like, I had better get used to it. Otto cannot be relied upon any more, since he's off fighting his own battles, and I have few friends to depend on who are not themselves trying to find shelter. So it is, I think, best to turn to one's own resources now, and not to expect or even hope for others to do the protecting. That goes for religion too.

It's been difficult this year to travel, since Jews are being forcibly ejected from Germany, and not accepted into Poland. Since Hitler seems to want to clear the Jews out of his fatherland, there have been trainloads of families and orphaned children sent abroad. Refugees leaving Germany have been accepted into England and America, but the Vatican has a new pope and there is speculation that he is a supporter of the Nazis. Italy too has a fascist for a leader, and it's becoming harder to find countries prepared to protect us. We were forced to apply for travel visas to visit Vichy and I'm concerned about whether the German border guards will be allowing Jews to travel freely through Berlin this week. It's impossible to know in advance of our train journey, and equally unsafe to remain in France, where our visas are valid only for our vacation.

As we came out of the synagogue, I saw a swastika painted on the front wall, and some street urchins were spitting at the old lady who came out ahead of us and shuffled to the street. I was tempted to shout at them and chase them away, but of course it is no longer safe to do that. It is unlikely that anyone would come to my rescue if they had turned on me, or worse, on Anna. I held her close and we turned away from the incident, but I saw from the corner of my eye that they were advancing on us across the pavement, and while Tom and Max are both strapping lads, I would not want them to participate in a street fight to protect Anna and me.

We might have been exposed to the same hateful treatment as the old lady, had not a gendarme been passing and shooed them away. I certainly didn't detect much anger in him, though. I suppose it's an everyday occurrence outside the synagogue, and there have been many much worse incidents reported in the press: beatings, and even killings in the streets, by Hitlerjugend and the Brawnhemden in Germany.

At least we didn't see such behaviour in Krakow before we left in July, though I do remember Tomasz telling me about some boys in his class at school who had joined the National Radical Camp after the anti-Semitic riots in thirty-six. He said they'd threatened Max in the playground and Tom had hit one of them in defense of his brother. At least Tom was a strong boy, and stood up to them, but you don't know how these feuds escalate, and what the parents of those boys would be like. I would have intervened with the headmaster, had we not been about to pull them both out of the school anyway.

We hurried away from the synagogue and managed to find a taxi to take us back to the Georges Cinq, where we would spend one more night before the boys were to take the boat train. After the incident outside La Victoire, I wanted to leave Paris. It felt like the end of a long summer, and having reconciled myself to returning to Krakow, I wanted to get on with it.

"Please can we go to the theatre, as it's our last night, Mummy?"

Anna always loved ballet and opera, and the Palais is certainly one of the greatest opera houses in Europe, and I thought this an admirable suggestion. We stopped at the concierge's desk on our return to the hotel to ask what he could tell us about the availability of tickets.

"Madame, I would love to be able to arrange tickets for the Palais Garnier, but unfortunately it has closed its doors this week and will not open again for a month. Perhaps I can make reservations for you in the restaurant?"

In the event, we stayed in the hotel for our last evening before the long journey. Anna packed her own trunk, with the maid's help, and then took a bath before agreeing to go to bed. The boys were reading in the lounge, and I had to pack for them, to make sure they would not leave half their clothes behind them, since neither was interested in domestic chores. By the time I retired, it was late and I was tired.

CHAPTER 6

Nord Express

There was only one way to make the journey to Krakow, by the Nord Express train through Germany, as the alternative that takes the southern route through Italy was not running. The next morning, which was the morning of August 24th, Anna and I accompanied Tom and Max to the Gare du Nord terminus so that they could catch the boat train to Calais, to connect with the ferry to Dover. Tomasz had sensibly purchased return tickets in London, but it took quite a long time for them to get through the barrier to the platform, as the guard who was checking tickets was flanked by two soldiers inspecting everyone's travel visas. We said goodbye on the concourse, but waited for them to pass through the barrier. Watching the process immediately made me worry about the journey East. Everyone in the queue looked concerned, and there were no pleasant exchanges.

Eventually they were though the barrier and onto the platform. We said our final goodbyes through the bars on the gate. I was holding back my tears, and wondering, as I'm sure they were, when we would next meet. I said "till Christmas" to Max, and firmly believed that they would both be able to travel to Krakow to join us by the end of their school term. There's no point being pessimistic about the future. I had already made up my own mind that if everything was in good order in Krakow, and Ania and Paul were happy to stay at home and look after things, I might travel direct to London through Rotterdam or somewhere further north, and to hell with Otto's demands. I didn't want to raise Tom and Max's hopes by telling them the plan, but it seemed altogether possible.

Once they had safely boarded and we'd waved them off, I went to the ticket office to buy our own train tickets. Already there were soldiers asking questions and checking the papers of the travelers in the long queues. We had been waiting about fifteen minutes, when we were approached by a mild-mannered man in French military uniform.

"Bonjour Madame. Where are you travelling to today?" He held out his hand for my identity papers, assuming I was French. I showed my own and Anna's passports, and as he inspected them, he eyed me more suspiciously.

"So, you are from Poland. Are you returning?" Although our passports didn't indicate that we are Jews, it might have been in his mind, even though I'm not obviously Semitic.

"Oui Monsiour. We will be taking the Nord Express tonight, if we can ever purchase our tickets. Is there any problem with the line?"

"Not to my knowledge, Madame. It may take time to clear customs at the Belgian and German borders, and certainly it will be full." And with that, he passed along the line, and I was able to return our papers to my handbag without further thought.

The summer heat was insufferable, and I could fully appreciate why the Parisians would want to decamp to the coast at this time. Anna was well behaved, but clearly bored, and she managed to find an iron railing to lean on while I queued. For the first time, after making this journey regularly over many years, I was quite worried. I understood that everything I had read over the summer pointed to trouble ahead for us, even in our familiar homeland. Perhaps, if there was no opportunity to travel to London, we could use Otto's contacts in Krakow to obtain travel visas to a neutral country, like Switzerland. The Epsteins talked about relocating to Switzerland, or America, when we were in Vichy. They are very wealthy, and well connected, and Aaron certainly didn't seem too concerned for their safety. But first I must get home to connect with people we can trust. Otto would of course be in a much better position than me to source appropriate documents, if he wasn't in Rumania with his bloody regiment.

In front of me, two elderly Germans were about to buy tickets to Berlin and seemed very anxious to leave. Although I am not fluent, I could tell they were worried about how they might be treated by the French if they stayed. It was apparent that they'd been asked to leave their hotel and were avoiding the gaze of others waiting for tickets. It strikes me that everyone is so paranoid nowadays, even looking like a Jew will be enough to get one bullied or ejected from a country, and these Germans were clearly not Jewish, but being encouraged to leave because of their nationality and the politics of their leader.

Our train will travel through Berlin, and of course that means stopping in the city of Hitler's headquarters. Apparently it is brim full of troops and their secret police, the Gestapo, who wear black leather coats and have a terrible reputation. It feels like we will be entering through the gates of hell, and I have visions of the three-headed Cerberus guarding the border.

Once we finally managed to buy our tickets, which involved showing our papers again, we had three hours to wait. I had already arranged for our baggage to be brought from the Georges Cinq and delivered one hour before departure to the gate for our platform, and they are very reliable. I managed to find the porter for our carriage to tell him what luggage to expect and that it would be arriving in the van belonging to the hotel. I explained that the trunks should be loaded, and that he should then find us in our compartment to confirm this had been done, before departure, which he agreed to do. I have learned from bitter experience that if the porter is not clear about one's baggage, he is apt to leave it sitting on a trolley in the station as one leaves for another country. He pocketed the ten Franc note and would expect another for arranging dinner and having our beds made up. Some people consider this excessive, but I always find that if one tips properly, one can rely on the guards to sort out all manner of small problems, and even to prioritise one's needs above those who tip less well.

We decided to have some early dinner in Terminus Nord, rather than venturing into the maze of backstreets that surround the station, as this area is none too safe after dark. There is an entrance from the station directly into the hotel, and we were served an excellent meal. I was only disappointed that Anna picked at her salmon, considering that so many people have too little to eat, and we will be travelling for the better part of two days before we're settled in the apartment and having Celestyn's home-cooked food. My sea bass was exceptional, and the waiter was most accommodating. Once we'd refreshed ourselves, the luggage arrived as arranged, and we were able to board. This is one of the best-kept trains after the Orient Express, and I have always enjoyed travelling across Europe on it.

The compartment was paneled in teak, with leather covered bench seating on each side, and on each wall were the clever contraptions for converting the headrest into a top bunk bed. Max and Tom used to love playing with those when we travelled from Krakow in the past, provided we had a compartment to ourselves. I could top and tail them on one top bunk and Anna would have the other, while Otto and I would take two lower couchettes. This time, though I hoped we would have the place to ourselves, it seemed unlikely, given the queues for tickets.

Our guard was most courteous, and the couchettes were clean, but I knew we would get little sleep as this train would be stopping in Brussels, Cologne and Hanover before it reached Berlin early in the morning. I was told by the guard that we should expect at least three hours' stopover in Berlin, and possibly more. Assuming all went well there, The Express would continue on to Frankfurt, before leaving the country on its journey east. I've never been particularly attracted by Berlin, though we spent some time there in the twenties. For me it is a somewhat claustrophobic and overbearing city full of ponderous buildings and grand boulevards. The last time I had been was in '36 or '37, and then it had an air of decadence, which I didn't approve of. I'm not particularly prudish, but the city had by then begun to get a reputation for sleaze, something that we had never experienced in Krakow. Nobody seemed to care whether they were seen cavorting in the streets. When we were first married, Otto took me to some night clubs, while on a weekend visit, and I remember the prostitutes queuing on the street outside, to be taken into the warmth by men who arrived, alone or in small groups, in evening dress after their theatre or restaurant engagements. One club I remember was called The Femina, which was on Nurnberger Strasse. It was a huge subterranean dance hall, full of smoke and smelling of drink. Each table had a telephone installed on it so one could call people seated at other tables, to proposition them, according to Otto. I suspected even then that he had been there with his father and made use of the phone. The night we were there, we stayed for a glass of champagne and watched a lurid floor show involving scantily clad women dancing in a line, something they must have taken from the Folies Begere in Paris.

For myself, I much prefer Salzburg and Vienna, with the opera and their wonderful coffee houses, and my memories of Austria for skiing and shopping are fond. Sadly, since Fascism took hold of the city, it is simply not somewhere to visit any longer. I hope that can change. I have a dear friend there whom I would like to see more often. Alexandre owns the most splendid restaurant in Vienna, and he is the finest, most chivalrous, handsome man I have ever met.

We were expected to show our papers at every station, according to the French soldier I spoke to, who had worked for the railways before enlisting. We didn't ask him whether Jews would be allowed to travel through Berlin, though I badly wanted to know what to expect. It seemed somehow too personal, and certainly not something we wanted to broadcast to those in the queue for tickets who might see all their problems with Germany as a Jewish provocation. Our visas do not state the fact that we are Jewish, though I understand that all visas issued in Germany do so. Many nations are not accepting German Jewish immigrants any longer, since so many have been deported and all the surrounding countries are bursting at the seams. Tomasz told me that Britain is erecting internment camps for Jewish refugees. How horrible! It certainly undermined my intention to travel there. I am pleased that he knows his way around in London. I would hate to imagine him being picked up by some over-zealous policemen and carted off to a detention centre! I often wonder whether one can disassociate from a religion that one is born into but which one no longer adheres to. Being born a Jew, these days, might be more of a mill-stone than an identity. Otto and I have never been devout, and I would have no personal concern about being identified as an agnostic or even an atheist, should it come to documenting my orientation.

We found our seats and made ourselves as comfortable as possible. Our compartment was supposed to be ours alone, but after a short time, as I expected might happen, we found ourselves sharing with four, then six others, including an elderly Belgian couple, two German officers in SS uniforms and a young couple who may have been Czech or perhaps Rumanian. It was hard to tell where they were from as they spoke in whispers, and held one another's hands tightly. The Germans got on in Brussels, and I was surprised to see Nazis in their uniforms in Belgium. I didn't realize that they were to be found abroad, armed and looking like they owned the place.

I had encouraged Anna to carry her small satchel with a book and some coloured pencils for the journey, but she was unable to settle to her drawing, and kept whispering banal questions to me, and not listening to my answers. I gave up trying to read my book and told her to be quiet. She really is at a difficult age, somewhere lost between childhood and adolescence, and she is uncomfortably shy among strangers. In the compartment, she hid behind my coat as though she were a four-year-old.

"For goodness sake, Anna, pull yourself together," I whispered. "These people won't bite you, you know."

We both studied the other passengers with caution. In fact, everyone eyed everyone else with suspicion, and it wasn't until we'd been sharing the space for an hour or more that the tension began to ease. Nobody except the two Germans spoke much to one another, and certainly not to those they didn't know. After eyeing each other up and down, we each turned in on ourselves to try and sleep. The soldiers chain-smoked and talked quietly of their time in Brussels. I tried to follow what they were saying in case it was relevant to our trip, but they were only discussing their commanding officer in derogatory and foul terms, so I gave up and dozed.

The train had left Paris on time, but once we crossed into Belgium, the journey seemed a great deal slower than usual. Though we both slept for perhaps an hour at a time, we were woken by the guard at every station, to show our papers, as we had been told to expect. The Belgian border checks were slow, and then we stopped in Bruxelles Nord for about fifteen minutes while German soldiers checked our travel visas and passports. Again, I found myself wondering why, in peacetime, soldiers were involved, and Germans at that. Clearly there was some kind of agreement between the Belgian railways and the German authorities to allow this, since the train was headed for Germany.

At the German border, there were dozens of soldiers in grey uniforms and some Gestapo police in their black leather coats checking people's documents carefully. The platform was dimly lit, and when I lifted the blind, I could see armed men every few metres along it, as well as men marching up and down in pairs or groups of four and six. In most cases, they were led by officers, but there were several men in the black leather trench coats, even though it was not cold.

Everyone watched nervously out of the windows as they paced up and down the platform under the station lights. The policemen in our carriage took several people off the train, handing each person down onto the platform into the clutches of two soldiers. This happened quietly, without fuss or complaint, until one man struggled to escape the grip of the two soldiers who had him by the arms. He was a respectable looking gentleman in his forties I would say, in a tweed suit and homburg. It seemed that his family was still on the train, and that was why he was resisting arrest. He kept looking back towards our carriage, and I thought I could hear a child's cries from a compartment two or three down from ours. This made him more agitated, and he fought to free himself so he could go back to his family. He began shouting at the soldiers to let him go and struggling against them. He managed to escape the hold of one of them, and made to return to the train, but the other was a burly soldier with an iron grip, and he was clearly ready for a struggle. While he held the man tightly, the first soldier pulled his rifle strap from his shoulder, lifted the weapon high and struck the man between the shoulder blades with the butt of it, there in front of us. The man fell to his knees, right outside our compartment, with a dull groan. It was shocking to see, and I held Anna to me and covered her eyes, but I was mesmerized by such violence, and watched as they picked the man up again and dragged him into an office. There were other incidents further down the platform, which we couldn't see clearly, and at one point I heard a woman cry out the name of her child, as she was pulled from the train.

Soon, I could hear compartment doors being slid open, and when it came to our turn, the doorway was filled with a huge young man in SS uniform, who looked like a gymnast or footballer, He had a very short haircut, a square jaw and blue eyes which barely moved beneath the grey metal helmet he was wearing. He stepped aside to let a Gestapo policeman pass into the compartment. This man was older, and had thin white hair, and a pinched face. He exuded menace, and his attention to each traveler and their papers seemed intense. He asked us whether we were planning to disembark at any point in Germany, and I said 'no' rather than mention our intention to leave the train in Berlin. He examined the papers of all the travelers except, of course, those of the two officers, who didn't bother to look up or break their conversation to acknowledge the intrusion. I was surprised that the Gestapo man didn't ask what our purpose for travel was. In fact, he seemed to be checking only that our papers were in order, and that none of us was disembarking in Germany. It was a slow process, but eventually the whistle was blown and the train groaned and shuddered before lurching out of the station. I breathed a great sigh of relief as we gathered speed, and actually exchanged a smile with the young Czech woman, who was obviously extremely nervous throughout the ordeal.

Besides the two officers from our compartment, who disembarked in Cologne, I saw very few travelers leaving the train at the stations we stopped in through Germany. The young couple went to find the restaurant car, and then there were only the two of us, and the old couple. They didn't do more than smile kindly at Anna, who was by that point asleep across my lap. I sat on in silence, in the light of the wall lamp, and tried to sleep. Anna and I should, by rights, by now have been asleep in our couchettes, with the compartment to ourselves. But with all the stops and the very full compartment, it wasn't appropriate to unfurl the bedding, and we agreed with the guard that we would wait until after Berlin to see if there was more space. As a consequence, for those last three or four hours before our arrival, I was unable to sleep and resigned myself to a wakeful night. The train stopped twice more in the German countryside, in the middle of nowhere in pitch darkness. Each time, there were clicks and groans and the distant hissing of steam, before an eerie silence covered the train like a blanket.

Pulling the blind away from the window, I couldn't see any lights or other sign of human habitation, though I pressed my face to the glass. Even in the silence of that night, and without any cause, I had a great sense of foreboding about our destination.

When we finally pulled into Berlin in the early light of morning, the suburbs looked no different than last time I had travelled through. As we approached the Anhalter Bahnhof station, it was as though we were floating into the mouth of a magnificent whale. The noises under its vast roof were magnified, and train whistles, hissing steam and shouting drowned out all else. The guard for our carriage passed the open door to the compartment.

"Guten Morgen, Frau. We will be here until 9.30am at least, but I would advise you to return to the compartment soon after nine."

"Danke schön."

The elderly couple opted to stay on in the compartment, even though there would be three hours' delay here. They clearly had no reason to leave the train and were probably terrified of setting foot in Berlin. I woke Anna and tidied her few belongings into the satchel while the train pulled to a stop and released clouds of steam into the morning air.

While in Vichy, I had been told by the Epsteins that Olek was in Berlin, apparently waiting for Maryla to join him from Krakow. We'd exchanged telegrams whilst I was at the Georges Cinq, as it occurred to me that I would possibly see Maryla before he did and I wanted to know if he planned to come to Krakow soon, and whether he had any messages for her. When he heard I was travelling home on the Nord Express, he knew I'd be stopping for a while in Berlin and he had asked if we would meet him there during the break in our journey. He would meet us off the train and advised that we go with him to an Hotel, as the Anhalter Bahnhof station was not a safe place for Jews to spend any time. Dieter Koch had travelled to France through Berlin only two weeks previously, and when we met in the Hershey, he told me that the place was crawling with police and soldiers, and there was no longer any restraint or recrimination among them for open violence towards Jews, even in public places. He'd seen one or two very nasty incidents that he was loath to describe, but I gathered they involved beatings and even one shooting of Jews in the station.

Although it was still only becoming light when we pulled into Anhalter, Anna woke fully and was keen to meet 'Uncle Olek'.

"I'm hungry. When are we having breakfast, mama?" she whined.

"You should have eaten your dinner. Now go and visit the cloakroom, before we meet Uncle Olek, and take my hairbrush. You look like you've been dragged through a hedge backwards! He will be waiting for us and he doesn't want to see his favourite girl in such a state."

"Will Aneta be with him?"

"No, my dear, she's with her mother, and we're going to see her when we get home."

Anna and Aneta were friends, though there was a year between them. Anna thought Aneta rather babyish and not at all interested in fashion or boys, but faced with adult company, Anna always looked for another child to play with. It's a shame that her brothers are much older than her and less engaged than one would like. Anna is quite an introverted child, and prone to moodiness. It must be a stage she's going through. Perhaps she's about to begin her periods, although she isn't developing anything of chest, and she still has such childish features. I have, of course, given her the facts of life, and I don't think she was particularly concerned about the possibility that she would have women's problems, but I do wonder sometimes how much notice girls take of this information until it actually begins for them. I assume it is the same for boys. I left it to Otto to talk to Tomasz and Max when they were preparing for their bar mitzvahs, but of course I never heard how that went. Neither of them has had a girlfriend to my knowledge, but of course it isn't possible to keep watch over their activities in London, and it wouldn't be my place to do so anyway. I did watch Tom closely in Paris to see if he exhibited any of Otto's traits, or, God forbid, Lolek's fascination with the opposite sex, but he seemed quite oblivious to the young Parisian girls.

CHAPTER 7

Berlin

When we disembarked, we left our luggage in the hands of the German guard, who assured us that nothing in his van would be touched while we were waiting to board again, as it had a locked cage in which our bags were stored, and only he had the key. One thing you can certainly say about the Germans is that they are very trustworthy on day-to-day matters and would not attempt to tamper with the luggage. That's not something I could say about the Poles with my hand on my heart, at least not the class of Polish worker who hangs around in the stations.

Anna saw Olek waiting at the barrier as soon as we stood on the platform and waved to him enthusiastically. She was disconcerted at his lack of response and continued to try and gain his attention. He did not wave back, though he clearly saw us, and it was only when we were a few yards from him, queuing to go through the gate, that he signaled with a surreptitious shake of the head for us to follow him across the concourse to the exit. He strode ahead of us so that we had to move quickly to follow him in the crowds. Once out of the station, on the Askanischer Platz, he kissed me on both cheeks and holding me then at arms-length in a fatherly appraisal, he smiled at me.

"My apologies for the cloak and dagger stuff in there, my dear. It has become dangerous to draw attention to oneself in public places here. Yesterday, I came to the station to check on the time of your arrival and witnessed a group of Jewish women, recently off the Nord Express, herded into a police van. I could see no reason for their arrest, and it is clear that the Jews are being rounded up for deportation, without ceremony or excuses. I've been here for two weeks and frankly, each day is worse than the one before. But enough of all that. It is wonderful to see you and you are both looking so well. Anna, my little angel, how are you and how was Vichy? Happy Birthday, by the way. I have a little something for you, but you must wait till we are somewhere more comfortable to open it. Let's find somewhere to sit and talk."

Olek is a tall, grey-haired, slim man with a high forehead and steel-rimmed glasses. Like me, he doesn't look particularly Jewish, and he always dresses carefully. He was wearing a herringbone three-piece suit, a heavy overcoat, and homburg, despite the late August warmth. I realised that his style was a sort of armour against being treated with anything less than the greatest respect. Staff in the station and the hotel bowed slightly to him and held open doors, which certainly would not have happened if he had less gravitas, since it was evident they didn't actually know him. The doorman even clicked his heels in the way of the Prussian Fusiliers, which was in fact appropriate, since Olek fought in the Austro-Hungarian army during the Great War. It is hard to imagine him in the epaulets and dress uniform now, but at least he's sensible enough to act his age and not to go trying to enlist again.

Olek ushered us into the foyer of the bustling Excelsior, full of men in SS uniforms, standing in circles and talking loudly, laughing and joking. The place was full of Berliners out for breakfast, or on their way to work, who seemed indifferent to the presence of the military men. It must have been like this throughout the summer, since Berlin has been like an army base for months, according to Dieter. We'd managed to avoid Germany on our journey west to Vichy, by travelling though Belgrade and Trieste, because I so much enjoy the views from the train as it travels along the Riviera.

I know that Berlin has always been a city with a purpose, and now I could see how focused everyone was. There was no lounging or loitering. Everyone had somewhere they had to be or someone they needed to talk to. In a way, this sort of energy has always attracted me, but now it has an edge, which I don't like. Everyone is glancing across at each other. They always seem to talk in slightly mooted tones, or positively whisper in one another's ears. There is an aggressive hierarchy among the soldiers, which is so obvious in the way one man expects another to hold open a door for him or run his errands. Officers barely deign to acknowledge their underlings when spoken to, and the more epaulets and medals and stripes a man has on his clothing, the more his nose points to the ceiling in an effort to look down it on everyone.

We managed to find a table in the restaurant where we could talk and Anna could have something to eat, albeit sandwiched between a business breakfast meeting of seven or eight Berliners in suits, and a group of officers hunched over their food. Everyone had that air of purpose and the waiters moved quickly between the tables. There were, I noticed, few women in the restaurant.

Olek was barely whispering, in Polish, trying not to be overheard by either group. His whole demeanour was furtive.

"You look well, my dear. The weather in Vichy has given you a fine colour, and I trust that your stay at the Hershey was as enjoyable as ever. I'm so pleased that you are here safely. I'm sure that the journey from Paris has not been easy."

"Thank you, Olek, it was both an enjoyable break and a reasonable journey, though I don't need to tell you how worried everyone is. The Epsteins send their best wishes, and Dieter Koch asked me to let you know that he will be in touch about the mahogany shipment as soon as he has more information. He said you would know what he means."

"Yes, thank you. He has been trying to arrange a delivery for weeks, but it is proving impossible to move anything by sea at the moment, as even the freighters are being re-deployed for military purposes. But let's not talk about timber. I hear from Otto that you are going to arrange to meet with Ania and Paul when you arrive tomorrow. I have to warn you that since you left in July, Krakow has become a very nervous place to be. I don't recommend you stay longer than necessary."

"Is Maryla there, Olek? Is she keeping the children at home? Why are you not returning? Surely you're not as crazy as Otto to want to enlist."

"No, my dear, I'm far too old, and besides, I am a great deal better off being in Danzig in order to obtain papers for Maryla and the children. It's impossible to get an official to sign anything in Krakow, and the city is effectively evacuating. I really wanted to counsel you to find a safe place in the country. Would you consider travelling on to Naleczow and staying in our summerhouse, or perhaps you'd like to visit the Uzdropwisko Spa there until things settle down a little? I sent Maryla word that she should go there."

"I have just spent several weeks in the spa at Vichy, so why would I want to go to another? I just want to be at home for a while. You know, re-engage with our friends and look after Anna's schooling. She's becoming a young lady and needs to be educated. Surely we can remain in Krakow until this all blows over?"

"I'm afraid I don't know the answer to that. I just don't see it being possible to step back into the lives we have led until now. Nothing is as it was a few years ago and I'm certain that for people like us, it will not be possible to keep our old lives. From here, it is clear to me that troops are being sent to Poland, and I cannot see how the new Russian agreement means anything other than invasion from both the East and West. "

"I was planning to go to London to stay with Tom and Max, you know, but Otto insisted we return to Krakow. Do you understand his demand, Olek? I mean, is there something I'm missing in his thinking? I am very worried, as you are, by the stories in the newspapers, and I frankly don't understand why he made this demand."

"We haven't been able to talk for a while, but I know that Otto feels the family should be together, and that you should be at home, rather than stranded abroad, should there be war. I know that he would want to be with you, but he also feels strongly about his role in defending Poland. None of us were nationalists, any more than any of us is a good Jew." Olek was barely whispering.

"But when we are threatened in this way, I believe, and Otto does too, that we should be ready to protect our homes, our families."

"What nonsense! I'm sorry Olek, but you are trying to obtain papers to get Maryla out of Poland, while Otto is outside the country insisting that I return. Besides, he's far too old to be joining up, and he would be a great deal better off protecting his family by keeping us out of harm's way in London than basing himself in Rumania to defend Poland!" I couldn't help raising my voice, and two or three of the businessmen at the next table looked in our direction, though thankfully, the officers were so engrossed in their breakfast they didn't notice my outburst. Olek, in his normal reticent way, placed his hands gently on mine and made a face that showed his pain and unease, but also his understanding of my frustration. He reached into his breast pocket and took out a manila envelope.

"This is for you. It is not much, but it's all the Zlotys we had in the Danzig office and what I brought with me. You will need to hold on to cash, as the banks will be closed, I've no doubt. I could have laid my hands on plenty of Reichsmarks but unless Germany takes over Poland, God help us, you won't need those." Olek's dry humour didn't raise a smile on his face or mine. "Make sure that you travel with any jewelry or gold you have and keep it close. I'm sure that in times like this you will need liquid assets and not fine china or pictures. Please, Miriam, for all our sakes, look after yourselves and take no risks.

"It will be important to keep in touch, as I will also investigate visas for you and Anna. As you know, I have my diplomatic papers, which I have used to apply for Maryla and the children to join me, but nothing is guaranteed. Otto will also be investigating the opportunities from wherever he is based."

"I hope you can come and help us soon, Olek. I really would not be going home if Otto hadn't insisted, and frankly, I am not hopeful that we will be left alone once we return."

We sat in silence while Anna finished her breakfast and I my coffee. Olek gave Anna a small package wrapped in brown paper, and when she opened it, it turned out to be a miniature music box. The lid was inlaid with mother of pearl flowers and it seemed to be made of polished hardwood. Anna's face lit up and it was a pleasure to see her smile after the misery of the last day or two. When she opened the lid, it played Clair de Lune, in a tiny soft chime, and it brought tears to my eyes.

"Thank you so much Uncle Olek," Anna flung her arms round his neck in an uncharacteristically warm gesture.

"It is charming, Olek, you must have had a difficult time finding it."

"Actually, it wasn't hard. It was in Strauss jewelers. They are closing down and were selling off everything they couldn't carry with them. Levi managed to buy tickets on the SS Washington out of Hamburg and they all left three days ago. I was passing on the day before they left, and the place was empty, other than a few clocks and trinkets like this. It was so sad. They've been here since the 1860s. There were Swastikas painted on the windows and the Star of David daubed on the door. I think they are the lucky ones too. On both sides of their shop, the windows were smashed and the shops looted."

I hadn't the appetite to eat my eggs, or even the pastries I am usually so fond of, and Olek had only ordered himself coffee. The officers got up and left, and the businessmen were also calling for the bill.

"Miriam, I wanted to ask you to look after Maryla for me. You are so much stronger and more independent than she is, and I know she looks to you for support."

I really didn't expect Olek to ask this of me. After all, he knows that I have stopped meeting Maryla regularly in recent months, ever since the rumours of her affair with Otto started circulating openly. Olek has never said anything to me about what people are saying, though he must be as aware as I am of them. I first heard the story from an extremely nosey neighbour who had told my hairdresser, who cannot keep a secret. She was looking so despondent when I sat for my weekly appointment that I quizzed her and she told me. That evening, I challenged Otto, who blankly denied it, and we have not had an open conversation since. But that's because I have hardly seen Otto in Krakow, and it is not for the want of trying. He's been travelling a lot more than usual and keeping a low profile when he is home. Since the boys moved to London, he spends very little time at the apartment. If I had wanted to have a show-down with him, it would have been very hard to get together for long enough. But when I examined my reaction to the gossip, I realized that I don't want to break our marriage up at the moment. It would be bad for Anna, and I'm not sure it would be good for me, given the way Otto fights his corner when it comes to money. As far as I'm concerned, the status quo is adequate in the circumstances. It works better for me not to be confronted with his probable infidelity every day. But that is by the by. As a result of these tensions, the last time the four of us got together socially was about nine months ago, and Olek has not once raised any concern about it, or pushed for an evening out or dinner, which means he knows, of course.

"Oh Olek, my friend, you can rely on me. I will look out for her, and we will try to share responsibility for the children. Anna and Aneta are friends, and Szymon is very protective. He's the sort of boy who wants to be a man, though I'm sure it's all Maryla can do to stop him running away to join up. It will not be easy for us without you and Otto, but you must not worry about us. Frankly, it is you that I will be most worried about, here. We have family and friends in Krakow, and you have no security here. Berlin has changed immeasurably, hasn't it? I don't like the feeling here. It seems only a matter of time before all the Jews will be deported, and all the Gentiles will be in uniform. Please return to Danzig as soon as you can. I'm sure it will be safer there."

Despite the affair, I've always liked Maryla. She's a warm and gentle person, a good mother to her two lovely children, and I do feel protective towards her. Nevertheless, I do wonder just how much Otto is the predator and she the prey. She is several years my junior of course, and she comes across as very naïve about so many things, having always had Olek's complete protection from the practical aspects of life. But later, when I thought about this last breakfast in Berlin, it was clear to me that I mainly offered this help for Olek's sake. Olek has always been so kind to me, almost fatherly, and I value his friendship deeply.

Actually, I didn't expect it would be hard to find Maryla and her children, or that it would be necessary to leave Krakow, let alone being exiled from Poland. The Germans wouldn't want to remain with winter coming, and by the autumn, everything would be back to normal, I was sure.

CHAPTER 8

Krakow

After a largely uneventful day on the train from Berlin to Krakow, with papers being checked at every station and little, if any, conversation among our fellow travelers, Anna and I arrived into Glowny station as the sun began to set, on the evening of August 26th. It was a beautiful day and Krakow looked handsome in the evening light, as long shadows were cast by every tree and lamppost. The train was almost empty by the time we reached the Polish border, and returning home felt slightly anti-climactic in the event. I thought people would have been cheering and clapping that we'd got through safely to our destination. Instead of which we were all just tired from our journey. I'd even been short with Anna after the twentieth rendition of Clair de Lune and she had sulked for the last two hours, refusing to read, even. Once we'd crossed the border, it was heartening to see station names in Polish, and to look out across the cornfields, resplendent in the evening sun. The train chugged slowly into Glowny Terminus and I had a brief word with the guard about putting our trunks into left luggage. He was Polish, and I assume he had taken over from our German guard at the border, as I didn't recognise him. Needless to say, it took a five Zloty note to bring an ingratiating smile to his lips, and as I handed the note over, I thought of Olek's envelope and what a thoughtful man he is.

People queued quietly at the gate to show their papers to the soldiers who manned it. They were waving to relatives on the other side of the barrier and smiling to one another, clearly relieved. There was no tension, as there had been at every station on the way, though clearly, everyone getting off was Polish, and I recognised one or two faces from the Jewish quarter. We would normally have had Janek, the odd-job man, collect us, but I hadn't remembered to ask Celestyna to ask him when I telegraphed her about our return time. We'd be fine crossing town on foot.

I would arrange with Janek to collect the trunks in our car in the morning. I wanted to make sure the apartment was fine and that Celestyna was there to help us unpack before he brought them upstairs for us and cluttered up the dressing room. If Olek's worst fears were realized, we might be moving on quickly and there would be little point in unpacking. It might be sensible to pack some winter clothing, if we were to be stuck in the mountains for weeks, and to take out our smarter summer wear from Vichy. After all, it seemed unlikely that Anna's birthday dress would get any use in the coming weeks, and my ball gown would be better hanging up in my wardrobe than being dragged from one place to another. From what Olek had said, I should also spend time sorting through our valuables to decide what we could sensibly travel with, should the need arise. The portrait that Otto had commissioned of me, which hung over the fireplace in the lounge, something that we both prized highly, would have to stay. My diamonds and the pearl necklace he gave me for my engagement present could easily be locked into my small travelling portmanteau.

Janek is a big-boned, lumbering man in his forties, with tufts of hair in his ears and a strong tobacco smell about him. He lives next door to Celestyna and he's sweet on her, though I'm sure she isn't interested in him. If she were, she'd have him cleaned up and his ears shaved in no time! He doesn't read, unfortunately, so every request or message must be sent through her, but at least he is very compliant. She only has to ask, and he will do whatever she wants. He's as strong as an ox and thinks nothing of shouldering my trunk to carry it up a flight of stairs.

It was a beautiful evening, and we decided to walk home, as there was no sign of any cabs at the station. The park was surprisingly quiet, considering how the last rays of the sun still lit our way, and it was warm in the late summer air. The park keepers had clearly already gone home, and one or two couples were out walking, but not nearly as many people as I would have expected. Not a child was in sight, and only a few dog walkers passed us. I wondered whether I could still get a copy of Glos Narodu at the newsagent, but they said that there had been no papers for the last week. Mr Wiśniewski, the newsagent, who is normally such a gossip, had nothing to say. He looked tired and furtive, and besides raising an eyebrow when I asked for the paper, he gave me no more than a simple greeting. His shop looked empty, and I could see suitcases stacked in the back room, through the door behind the counter. I was going to ask him where he was going but thought better of it. One has to be careful to whom one talks about one's affairs. Olek was right.

We live on the second floor in one of the magnificent double-fronted 19th century houses overlooking the river. It's more of a villa than a town house, with a long front garden, a curved driveway and a pair of heavy iron gates and high railings alongside the pavement. The house has an elegant sandstone façade, which is intricately carved with cherubs and angels and there is even a coat of arms, though I have no idea whose it is. The whole street was rebuilt in the early eighteen hundreds, and our house was probably converted into apartments around the time of the Great War. We bought the place in '32, after we received a windfall from one of Otto's best timber deals with the Office of Public Works. I chose it for the views, and its beautiful high ceilings and fine plaster work. We spent quite a bit with our decorators and I had a fitted kitchen installed, with a modern range, which was quite a new idea, so that Celestyna could cook for large dinner parties in comfort. The house is around the corner from the plaza on Szeroka Street, where the restaurants and bars are so popular. Otto is convinced it has doubled in value, or he was until earlier in the year when he was told almost point blank by the estate agent that nobody wanted to buy a Jew's house except Jews, and that would depress the price. He would have taken offence, except the agent was himself Jewish and a regular in the synagogue, and clearly knew what we would be up against in selling. It had only been an idle enquiry, as we're very happy there, so no matter. We'll wait until this fascist wave has passed, and people return to a more equitable viewpoint. The neighbours are quiet and generally keep themselves to themselves, and it is in the perfect location for visiting friends, eating out, for schools and so on.

That evening, as we made our way home, many of the bars in the plaza were still thronged with people, and I had a moment of relief when I heard the familiar music they were playing and smelled the cooking from their kitchens. I thought for a moment that perhaps the nightmare we were all expecting was no more than a dream, and that everything was as it should be. But that was a rose-tinted view, and I knew in my heart it wasn't true. I could still remember the horrors of the Great War, and all those poor maimed men begging on the streets having lost their homes while they fought for freedom. I had no illusions about the ravages of war and what it might mean for Krakow, even if the fighting was short-lived. Since 1918, so much had advanced technologically, and for the first time, if Germany decided to invade us, they would dominate the air above us. The papers would have us believe that they would rain bombs on our heads which would destroy every building in the city and crush innocent people in an indiscriminate process of flattening their enemies. How a man can run at another with his bayonet and impale him on it is quite beyond me. It must be impossible to do that in cold blood. But pressing a button in an aeroplane and releasing a cargo of explosives may be as easy as switching on a light or ringing a doorbell. One wouldn't see the consequences of one's actions, presumably, since the warplane would have passed its target and one might be looking out over the rolling countryside before the bombs landed. Even if you circled round, to check the target, all you might see is smoke. You wouldn't be able to look at the bodies, or the body parts, flung across a street. You couldn't see the pain on the faces of parents whose children had been running for shelter and hit by shrapnel, or the devastation when your bombs blew apart some ancient monument or a hospital. It seemed to me that war might become very impersonal for the soldiers in such circumstances.

The newspapers had been reporting for months the sort of combat we might expect. Apparently, German Panzer tanks have been designed, and manufactured in their thousands, which can travel at up to 40 kilometers an hour, and can fire their guns up to a kilometer, and blow the side off a house. Hitler has been planning this for years now and it has been reported that he won't be satisfied with less than full-scale war, simply to prove his dominance. The generals and commanders will sit in bomb-proof war rooms, studying maps and planning troop movements, or calling up fleets of aircraft to fly over cities, and they won't see or feel the impact of their decisions. It will be a war run by hand-washers, but on the ground, it will be a carnage never before experienced.

I shook my head in an effort to shake these dark thoughts from my mind. There were many uniformed soldiers outside the bars, lounging against the walls, sitting on the railings and smoking. They were relaxed, and even though the were coarse and their language was inappropriate for Anna's ears, it didn't seem wrong that the place was overtaken with khaki and brown uniforms. I felt happy to be in my own neighbourhood again.

There was quite a lot of anti-semitic graffiti in the square, but that was nothing new. Any young hooligan in Krakow could turn up there late at night to deface the walls. But when we turned the corner at the end of our road, and approached the house, I was shocked to see a swastika daubed on our front gatepost, and the paint looked fairly fresh. I made a mental note to get Janek to scrub that in the morning.

It was a great relief to turn the key in our front door, and to put down my portmanteau and Anna's bag, which I'd agreed to carry from the station. The apartment was as I had left it, and thankfully Celestyna had prepared us a late supper of cold cuts before she went home. We were both ravenous after the long journey and ate in silence. Anna was exhausted and went to bed straight after supper. Once I was alone, I wandered through the silent rooms, admiring the furnishings I had spent so much effort on, picking up silver framed photographs of the boys and rearranging the flowers I'd asked Celestyna to buy. I opened the French doors and stood on the balcony of my bedroom, overlooking the river. I could hear the music from the square, and I felt peaceful, almost happy. But even then, I couldn't help but feel that my life had been overtaken by my duties, by Otto's expectations of me, and by parenthood. It felt as though I had never really had the chance to be an independent person in my own right. My friends in Krakow are mostly the wives of successful businessmen, who occupy themselves with spending money and giving parties. I've never had the chance to make my own way or achieve anything for myself. I'm intelligent and well educated, I have some business skills and I'm still young enough to make a change. I've only recently turned forty, and I can still turn heads, although I used to occupy the limelight as a younger woman. Otto has probably been unfaithful to me for years, and yet I've been faithful to him, with one exception, despite my never having loved him in a romantic way. Why is that? Perhaps I should have had more of my own adventures. And why did I obey him when it came to returning home? Was it because he knew best or because I couldn't bring myself to declare my independence? I am beginning to doubt my autonomy and individuality. I know in my heart that if I had gone to London against his wishes, he would have tried to cut me off financially, and assumed I wanted a separation or divorce. That's the way men of our generation see their wives; as chattels. We've never spoken of a formal arrangement, but I know Otto, and I know he would not want to be the accused. He would want to be the wronged party. Despite his infidelity, he would expect to be able to tell everyone that his wife ran off, his wife gave up on his devoted marriage. If he had ever found out about Alexandre, he would have been quick to mount an attack, to divorce me on the grounds of adultery. But that is long buried; it was years ago. It happened in the twenties, when the boys were young and it was at a low point between Otto and me. Unlike Maryla and him, which started then and has not stopped, as far as I am aware.

Alexandre Roskov was an Austrian restaurateur, whom I was introduced to by Stashek in Vienna when I was still in my twenties, when Max was a baby. It was at a time when Otto must already have been seeing Maryla, and everything between him and me was drifting apart. We had stopped sleeping together, and we were hardly talking except when we were both in company.

Alexandre was everything that Otto wasn't. He was tall and handsome, almost beautiful, and the most gracious and respectful man I think I have ever met. I knew the moment we first met that he wanted me as a lover, and had I given him the right signals, he would not have hesitated because I was married with young children. His dedication to me was obvious, and from the beginning, we became great friends, though I was certain he always wanted more. Our brief affair came later, and I was the one to end it, because I could not have it on my conscience and remain married, even though I felt sure Otto was continuing to play around.

There have, of course, been many others who have admired me. Otto's business associates, the fathers of Tom and Max's school friends and even the husbands of some of my neighbours and friends. But I am no longer young, and now I see no reason to demand a divorce. It wouldn't help the children, and with war on the way, it would be impossible to arrange anyway. Standing among my possessions, in my home, I felt trapped, and my responsibilities to the family were a huge burden.

The following morning, Janek collected our trunks from the station and delivered them to the apartment, and we decided to unpack because home is home and there was no immediate need to leave. I spent the next three days calling to all our friends' houses to see who was still in Krakow, who was intending to leave, who had stories to tell of friends and relatives of theirs in Germany and Austria who had already been deported, or who had escaped to America or Switzerland. They were three bitter-sweet days when re-connecting meant opening one's heart to the woes of others and trying to sound positive and optimistic. I dreaded ringing someone's doorbell in case they were crying when they answered it. I wanted to meet people for whom the future was bright, but nobody felt that way. It became a litany of other peoples' woes. Everyone wanted to know what I planned to do and I couldn't give a firm answer to that question. At the same time, I suppose I wanted to draw on their networks of information in order to make sensible decisions. It came down to the fact that those with business interests in Krakow, especially those involved in export, were keen to stay to try and run their companies at a time when foreign income was vital to their survival, but were concerned in case their workers stopped coming in to work, in case the banks stopped functioning so they couldn't pay the wages, in case their export markets dried up. Dieter Koch, who had returned from Vichy directly after I left, to protect his timber interests, had already lost a number of contracts because he was unable to travel to Germany to negotiate with customers, and those he was able to talk to on the phone or by telegraph, were suffering so badly that they had pretty well stopped ordering stocks. On the other hand, he knew of two or three Catholic owners who were winning big contracts from the German army for supplying equipment boxes and so on. Local shopkeepers were, like Mr Wiśniewski, packing up their belongings and leaving, because their local customers had already left town and there was precious little to display on their shelves anyway. Some were selling off the contents of their shops at rock bottom prices, others were putting them into storage, in the hope of returning soon. Altogether, Krakow was becoming a bit of a desert during the day, and the only businesses that were thriving locally were the bars in the plaza, which served soldiers. Even then, many of our troops were confined to barracks and others were being shipped out in convoys of army lorries, some to the east and others to the west. In the morning, we were woken by a continuous rumbling sound, like distant thunder, which turned out to be an endless stream of lorries driving past the house down the quays.

Anna's school was due to open on September 1st, but I received a note from the head teacher to say that so many parents of pupils had been in touch to tell him they were withdrawing their children for this term, because they were leaving the city, that he had been forced to suspend classes. Anna was not disappointed, as she doesn't love school, but I realized it would be one more change of arrangements to contend with. Normally, I would spend the mornings visiting friends and shopping, and in the afternoons, I might be at home to visitors. But Anna wasn't part of my social life, and it really wasn't appropriate to be traipsing around with a thirteen year old to listen to tragedies, and witness family strife. On the other hand, most of those I would have visited had gone, and I had only two or three callers in those afternoons, which I spent going through our belongings and trying in vain to get in touch with Otto to have him arrange with the bank to release funds to me.

The political news from abroad was sketchy and rarely proved to be factual. I had sight of a newspaper each day though it would be two days old and produced in Warsaw. Krakow newspapers had not returned, and the news from the capital was probably the best source of information because the radio stations were becoming very unreliable. According to the Nowy Kurier, German troops were amassing on the Polish border. A bomb was set off in Tarnow, which was apparently the work of a German agent, and it killed 20 people in the railway station. Britain was encouraging Germany and Poland to meet to agree Poland's security, and were warning that if we failed to negotiate our independence, we would undoubtedly end up at war. Hitler, it seemed, was prepared to negotiate with our government, but it wasn't clear from the report whether he would agree to leave Poland alone in the event of war. It seems that The Free State of Danzig was at issue and Germany was demanding that it be returned to German rule. I thought of Olek, who was probably there, and I thought of his request for me to help Maryla, who was meant to be in Naleczow, at the spa. Perhaps Olek was right about leaving Krakow quickly. It certainly felt like a ghost town, and I did promise to meet up with Maryla. I began to accept that it would be best to travel to Naleczow by car in the next week, along with Paul and Ada, Ania and Isidor, all the children, and Ania's housekeeper.

By the 31st, it became apparent that Slovakia had given in and accepted German rule two days earlier, and everyone now doubted that Poland would come out well from the talks our government was holding with Hitler. The local troops had almost all left the city, and now the plaza was very quiet in the evening. All the Jewish restaurants were shut, and each day, the owners were out with hammers and nails, boarding up the windows, since anti-Semitic vandalism was spreading across the quarter.

We'd been home less than a week, when Celestyna came to the door in tears. Once she had been brought in and given a handkerchief, and had calmed down a little, she told me that Janek had come to her an hour ago to tell her that Germany had invaded Poland. He had heard from his cousin, who had driven from the border city of Gleiwitz just ahead of the German army advance. Gleiwitz is a small town in Silesia, on the German side of the border, and it seems that according to German radio, Polish forces had icrossed the border and attacked a radio station there. That story didn't make any sense to me, but it had been a good excuse for the declaration of war by Hitler. Once the declaration had been made, the invasion started immediately, and apparently the Polish army was not prepared for the attack at daybreak. The General in charge had been waiting for some peace negotiations, which didn't take place, before he ordered the men to prepare, and of course they were taken by surprise. Janek's cousin told him that the journey to Krakow had been horrendous, and his car had been strafed by bullets from low-flying German fighter planes, which were also bombing the ground troops and civilians. Apparently, huge numbers of refugees had begun to pour out of the border towns travelling East towards Krakow. News preceded the onslaught like the blast before an explosion, and while there were no more newspapers with bulletins, or any obvious form of mass communication, it was amazing how the stories told by retreating Poles and returning travelers from the west became common knowledge. Celestyna, once calm, wanted to know what I planned, and though I offered to bring her with us to Naleczow, she declined, and said she would travel to stay with her sister. Janek would be staying in Krakow, and he would be able to keep an eye on the apartment for us.

The families who arrived by car were in the vanguard, as many refugees who left Silesia were on foot, pulling their possessions by horse and cart. There were stories being spread that many towns near the border had been set alight, and that before that, in each town, people were lined up in the town square or outside the town hall and shot. Apparently it wasn't just the Mayor or the able-bodied men, but women and children too. In Bedzin, hundreds had apparently been burned alive in their homes and in Piotrkow, the Jewish quarter was raised to the ground in a huge inferno, that spread so fast, many were trapped in the blaze and burned alive.

CHAPTER 9

Leaving Krakow

Jakub Kowalski was busy packing his car. He's my neighbour from the apartment below ours, whom I regularly meet in the front garden, which he likes to tend. I don't particularly like the man, as he is a bit of a nosy old fellow, and because he tends to have quite conservative views about most things. We are always civil to one another, but I think he disapproves of our dinner parties if we have the balcony doors open, and he complains about our car whenever it blocks the entrance.

"Are you leaving Miriam? Is Otto coming to take you to safety?" Jakub sounded extremely agitated. "I'm not waiting to be executed in Szeroka Plaza. It's the Jews they want, you know."

Jakub could be nervous at the best of times, and he was such a little man, with a huge wife, it was obvious to me that he had been hen-pecked all his married life. He looked to me like a rabbit in a car's headlights.

"My brother, Jan, came to me last night. He's from Czestochowa, and he was fleeing for his life. They have a car, because he's a doctor, and he was able to get away, but he told me of the atrocious things that the German soldiers did there. I can't repeat them to you, they are just too awful."

"Jakub, are you taking the family to visit your relatives in Lwow? Is it safe there? I was told by Otto's business partner that the Germans have agreed with Russia to divide up our country and that the Russians will undoubtedly move into Poland since Hitler is taking as much land as he can. I think that Lwow might become a Soviet occupied city."

"I'm leaving as soon as we're packed, and I advise you to do the same. Keep little Anna close. And your sister, Ania, is she here?"

"We have only been back a couple of days from France, and I am trying to find out whether she is at home. So far we haven't been able to contact her."

Jakub retired only last year from his civil service job, and his children have already left home, but his oldest boy, Filip, is in the army, and was sent to the Western front back in June. Jakub seems to have aged quickly since Filip went away, and he's had two heart attacks this year already. Though the day was not hot, he was sweating profusely as he lugged a large leather suitcase down the stairs to his car. It's only a small vehicle, and it was already laden down with a trunk on the roof rack. There was barely space inside for Agata and himself, as there were boxes on the back seat and what looked like ornaments and paintings stacked in there too.

"Come and have a cup of tea, Jakub. You look like you need to sit down and rest. You shouldn't be lifting those heavy cases. Are you emptying your apartment?"

"No, but we want to take our valuables to safety. If what Jan told me is true, the Germans will be here in no more than two days. You must make some plans."

Jakub couldn't be persuaded to rest, and his feverish activity marked the urgency to find Ania, and Maryla, as Olek had asked. We clearly couldn't stay in Krakow, and Celestyna had told me that she would not be able to continue working another hour, as she had bought a train ticket to Lublin to stay with her sister, so we would not have her help to pack up the apartment. I have given her the silver cutlery canteen and the Meissen to look after, as I know she will take great care of it and we cannot possibly travel with such items. That cutlery was a gift from my father on our wedding day, and the canteen is mahogany. Celestyna has promised that if she has to flee, she will bury everything in a safe place.

The Duesenburg was parked at the side of our building, behind Jakub's Fiat, and seemed to dwarf his car. We've had it for several years, and though it guzzles petrol, there is space for all five of us, and our luggage, when we go skiing in Zakopane. Well, when we went skiing, I should say. I can't see us all coming together as a family again for a long time to come. Now there are only Anna and me, and space for whatever we want to take with us. I made the decision on the spot to pack and have Janek come over first thing in the morning to load our bags. I tried once more to persuade Celestyna to come with us to Naleczow, where we would try to find Ania and Maryla and her children, but she declined, and I bade her a fond farewell, still hoping we would have her back with us for Christmas.

The day passed quickly and busily as Anna helped me gather those of our belongings which we could not do without. We had emptied our trunks of the summer beachwear and parasols we'd taken to Vichy, and now we replaced those inappropriate items with winter clothing, and all our most valuable possessions, which were easily carried. I decided not to follow Jakub's example and left behind the paintings and framed photographs, as well as many of my favourite ornaments. This exile would, with luck, comprise just a few weeks of autumn walks and a comfortable enough stay in the spa. If we found ourselves on the move again, then there was no point being overloaded with possessions.

Otto's desk was locked, and I had to use a kitchen knife to open the drawer where he kept his cash in a small metal box. When I had finally pried open the lock, I found very little cash to take, but with Olek's kind gift, we had enough money for a few weeks of living expenses, if we were careful. Already the food shops had very limited choice, and there was little point taking a large amount of fresh food to Naleczow, because it would only go off in the heat of the car. Besides, even with the war approaching, we should be able to acquire provisions along the way, especially in those small villages in the hills that always have such beautiful produce. I hope that the problems we are experiencing in Krakow will not spread to Naleczow. We've always enjoyed good treatment at the spa, and Anna can be so fussy with her food.

Early in the evening, the doorbell rang and I opened the door to Isidor, Ania's husband. We kissed and he came into the hallway, but didn't want to rest or have an early evening scotch, which was unlike him. I was so relieved to see him, though his face was a sorry picture of worry. He and Ania had been in Warsaw, staying with his mother, and he had been dealing with various problems at his offices. hey had decided to return to Krakow when Ania heard from Paul that I had returned from France. Isidor, a most capable man, with influential friends in government, told me that the country would not be able to defend itself from the Germans and Russians, and that he, Ania and their two boys were preparing to leave tomorrow, if we would travel with them. Paul and Ada were also getting their car ready, and we should make a convoy and drive to Naleczow. If the roads were clear, we would be there in the afternoon.

"It is so good to see you, Isidor. How is Ania and has Edmund got over his hayfever? I missed you all."

"Yes. My dear, everyone is fine. Ania will be so pleased to see you, after so long. She is quite depressed I think to be leaving everything behind. We are worried about leaving in a rush, and not having enough time to secure the property. I am hoping to persuade our handyman, Aleksander, to keep watch over our houses while we're gone. I'll ask him to check your place too, though I know you have that fellow who's in love with your cook, don't you? It may be impossible to stop those Bolshevic monsters from breaking in and rifling our things, of course. But we needn't leave our doors open. The Germans are a more disciplined bunch, but from what I hear, they're not taking any hostages."

"The Russians are coming to Krakow? Really, do you think so, Isidor? Did you hear something in Warsaw?"

"I heard that the government hasn't the stomach for a long fight and that the army is in some disarray on the eastern front. We can expect German soldiers here within two days and Russian troops are already massed on the borders of Belarus and Ukraine, so we can assume that our men will be forced back this way from the East. We have a big army, but nothing compared to the combined forces against us. They have agreed not to fight one another, so it will simply come down to which enemy reaches Warsaw first and where they divide our land."

Isidor always had that urbane wry humour and was prepared to make a joke out of most things, which I have to say is not an attractive trait, but he didn't even crack a smile. I was of course shocked, but I somehow didn't feel distraught or confused. I just knew I had to take responsibility for myself, and Anna, and let others work out their own response. I am known as such a strong and practical person, I frankly feel better without Otto there trying to run everything. Isidor and I agreed that we would take the three cars and slip out of the city first thing in the morning as fast as we could.

I finished our packing late that evening and fell exhausted into bed. I dreamed about a fire in the apartment, and I woke up smelling smoke. I was convinced that the lounge was on fire and that Anna would be overcome in her bedroom. I leapt up and ran through the whole place in my nightgown, convinced I would come upon an inferno, but everything was silent, and after a few moments, I heard the dawn chorus from the trees outside. I crept back to my room and lay in bed, wide awake, and thought about why I might have dreamt such things. I certainly was anxious about the day ahead, and about leaving this relative security behind. I was scared for Anna and myself, and I felt more depressed than I can remember about the twists and turns of my life. How could we be in this position when only a couple of weeks ago, we were enjoying dinner parties in Vichy and had plans for our futures. The silence of the early morning brought home to me the need to calm down and to take care of each moment as it comes. We might be about to uproot everything, to take ourselves out of our comforts, but we are strong, independent, intelligent beings with the ability to control our destiny, and also to rise above the awfulness of our circumstances. As I lay there, knowing that in an hour or two we would be leaving, I promised myself that I would look on whatever was given to me, and I would hold fast to my values and purpose. After all, there would not need to be accoutrements or plush comforts, financial security or predictable routines in order for Anna and me to come through this storm. I began to calm down and my heartbeat, which had been racing, slowed. I felt resolute and almost happy in the moment that this challenge brought. I rose again and padded barefoot on the thick carpets around the apartment, saying goodbye in my mind to all those beautiful polished surfaces, to the cut glass decanters, to the framed paintings and velvet curtains. It didn't feel like a wrench, or even a sad parting.

I dressed in comfortable clothing, nothing fancy. I'd have been tempted to wear trousers if I'd had some, but chose a tweed skirt and blouse, and a pair of sensible walking shoes. I boiled the kettle for coffee, made toast for Anna, and boiled a few eggs for the journey, before waking her and dressing her in her everyday play clothes and a pair of ankle boots which would withstand plenty of wear. It was still only six thirty and she was groggy with sleep.

Over breakfast I said:

"We're going to be driving all day today, darling, so you can catch up on your sleep in the car. It's the beginning of a big adventure, and I can't tell you where it will lead, but I want you to know it's going to be all right. We're travelling with Aunt Ania and Uncle Paul, and all your cousins, and we'll be meeting Aneta when we find out where she and Aunt Maryla are staying. I'm sure you'd prefer to be sleeping in your own bed, and playing with your toys here, since we've only just returned after the summer holiday, but we may be away for a while. You must be brave always and you must help the adults when asked. I will be with you all the time, and you needn't worry, even when you see things which might scare you."

"What sort of things? What will we be doing in Naleczow, Mamushu? Will I be going to school there? Will we stay in the hotel?"

"I can't tell you the answer to all your questions now, dear. All I can tell you is that it will be an adventure and you have to put your best foot forward. We'll see what we will see. Now, can you check you have everything you need for the journey in your satchel, and it will be your job to help Janek pack the car with your things. And can you pack our lunches into a shopping bag and include some fruit. You know it's good for you."

Celestyna had arranged for Janek to call early to help load the car, and he came at seven, silently doing what was asked of him, carrying my trunk and Anna's suitcase, plus a few other items in boxes, which I thought we might need. I'd packed our battery powered flashlight, some hand-tools I found in the cleaning cupboard, my writing box and stationery, some cutlery and crockery, a corkscrew, kitchen knives, and even a small hatchet, in case we had need of it. It all reminded me of my teenage camping trips in the mountains with Paul, and I wondered if he too would be packing his rucksack full of climbing gear.

We left at 7.30, and it struck me that this was the first time in years I'd actually driven myself in the Duesenburg. It's a huge, lumbering beast of a car and I'd far rather have had a smaller car for myself, but Otto has a mean streak and sees no use in us owning a second vehicle when we have people who can drive me about. He loves the Duesenburg, because, I think, it makes him feel important, but for me it is a throwback to a time when one had a chauffeur and arrived in state to balls and suchlike. Today, it was fairly full, and I was grateful for the space, but concerned that we would have difficulty buying petrol on our journey, since the newspapers had been reporting fuel shortages for months. The fuel tank holds vast amounts of petrol but seems to drink it extremely quickly. But here was the first example of something I should only try to deal with when it became a problem and something I should learn not to worry about until it was.

We'd arranged to meet the others on the main road, across the river, which was equidistant between our three homes. We were there at eight and waited no more than a few minutes for the others to arrive. With only a few words of greeting and a quick discussion about our planned route, we began our journey to Wilkolaz Pierwszy, where we found ourselves in a stream of traffic heading east. By the time we reached Rzeszow, we were at crawling pace, and we dared not stop for a rest in case we couldn't reach Naleczow in daylight. Most of the people already on the road were driving cars and lorries, but there were many people piling their belongings onto carts at the roadside, and by tomorrow, it would be impossible to make any headway. Luckily, we had our lunch packed and flasks of lemonade for Anna and her cousins, and coffee for me, so we didn't need for anything other than a toilet on the journey, and we arrived into Naleczow early in the evening without mishap.

CHAPTER 10

Naleczow

Despite the crowds of arriving evacuees, Isidor had managed to secure three rooms at the hotel, through his friendship with the Mayor. The car park was overflowing, and most of the cars were stacked high with luggage, because the hotel staff were clearly unable to cope with the influx of guests all at once. We took what we needed in an overnight bag and left the car locked with our bags inside. In the lobby was a huge crowd of people, all talking loudly to one another about their journeys. I recognised many faces from Krakow, but it seemed that Naleczow was a haven for a great many evacuees from cities and towns across the region. I could hear snatches of conversations about the mass exodus from Lublin, and even some early arrivals from Warsaw. We queued at reception for all of twenty minutes before we reached the desk, and the receptionists were polite but brusque. Once we had finally checked in and dropped our bags in the rooms, I went searching for people we know. The Steinbergs were staying, and the Epsteins, and I heard of several families we socialise with in Krakow who had arrived at their summerhouses and were taking in guests.

I was pleased to find that Maryla, Szymon and Aneta were already staying at the hotel, as I had expected, and had been in Naleczow for over a week. Maryla was well and fairly relaxed, considering the hubbub and scaremongering. It struck me that she was either much stronger than I had thought, or much less engaged with her surroundings than I was. I decided it was the latter, as she didn't seem to be very knowledgeable about the news which I'd been getting from the Warsaw newspapers, which I assumed they were getting here too.

"I haven't had the heart to read the newspapers, Miriam, and I rely on friends to tell me what they have heard. Many stories seem to be re-interpreted from moment to moment, so I have really stopped listening as much. Aneta has had a cough and I'm forever trying to find Szymon when he disappears off exploring the grounds, so it's as much as I can do to look after the children, without spending my time worrying about what might happen."

Everyone had heard about the declaration of war, of course, and that the German army had invaded Poland, but Maryla was vague about how far they had advanced and about Russia's intentions. She didn't know about Germany's plan to regain control of Danzig, and what that might mean for Olek and Otto. I was not surprised, though somewhat irritated, to discover that she had heard about Otto's decision to enlist in Rumania. I assume that she must have received direct news from him but decided not to enquire how she knew. We exchanged stories from the summer, and I was able to tell her about how Olek was coping in Berlin, and what he was hoping to achieve with regard to travel papers in Danzig. Despite my reassurances about our position, which I suppose sounded quite hollow, she managed to look quite helpless there, surrounded by the children and in the comfort of the lounge.

"Thank God you are safe, Miriam," she said. "I worried so much when Olek telegraphed that he couldn't get home, and he told me that Otto was also stranded in Danzig. But that is old news of course, as now Olek is in Danzig and Otto is with his regiment. What should we do?"

"I've only just arrived, and Isidor and Paul said they would try to find out more about what has happened in the last twenty-four hours before we re-assess the situation. Before we arrived, Isidor was of the opinion that we can't stay here for long. He believes that the German army will make quick headway in their advance from the west, and that the Russian army may invade from the east. That will mean we have to choose which is the least of the two evils, in case we are over-run."

"But the Jews are being targeted by Hitler for deportation, and I have heard nothing but horror stories about the way those Bolsheviks behave! We can't run and hide, but I can't imagine they will leave us a safe corridor in the middle. Do you think they will have some sort of no-man's land between their two occupied territories?"

"No, I don't think either enemy is going to act in an humanitarian way towards Poland. we clearly can't allow ourselves to be overtaken by the fascists, since Hitler has no qualms about subjugating the Jews. The Russians are not persecuting Jews more than any other people, to my knowledge, and I suppose we must also go where our army is strongest. We do still have the Polish forces defending us both sides, though it seems we have been pushed back in the west. Unless you have found more money than Olek expected, between us we haven't enough to pay for these hotel comforts for long. Olek made it clear that the banks are not going to continue to transact international payments for long. We must find more reasonable accommodation and then we must consider what the children can do about schooling. We may have to stay for some weeks."

In the event, we didn't stay long enough in Naleczow to find alternative accommodation. Isidor and Paul heard that the Germans would reach Lodz within a day, and that the Luftwaffe were already flying missions and bombing Warsaw. The Germans had taken Grudziadz and Mlawa, and had crossed the Vistula, when they met our army from Krakow just three days after we left. Although we would have remained in the spa town we all knew well, there was news every day of the German advances from Krakow in our direction from the west, and then within only two weeks, of the Soviet attack on Grodno, and of the Polish army giving way completely in Dubno and Luck. It seems that our forces thought the Russians were actually coming to save us from the Germans, against whom most of our large army was pitched. But clearly, they were hell-bent on taking our eastern provinces, as there were hundreds of thousands of Soviet soldiers massing on the Belarusian Front and as many on the Ukrainian border. We heard some of the news on the radio, until the radio stations were bombed by the Germans, and then we relied on the stories from refugees pouring into Naleczow every day. By the middle of that week, we were shocked to hear that our government had moved across the border into Rumania.

Isidor called a family conference at Paul's villa, which he was borrowing from some friends. He felt it was essential to make plans, because he had received news that we would be overtaken here within days by the advancing German army, who were committing atrocities wherever they went.

We felt that there was no choice but to continue east, towards the Russian army. We were caught in a strip of land that was being literally squeezed between invading forces.

"I suggest we aim for Lwow. It's only a day's drive in normal circumstances, and while it looks certain to fall to the Russians, there is every reason to expect Hitler will leave it alone. It is a large and well-fortified city with a substantial Ukranian population, and I am given to understand that Stalin has included it in his plans. I propose that we make for Lwow immediately and if necessary, keep travelling east until we are under Russian occupation." Isidor had always been clear and decisive, and for once I was happy to take his instructions without argument.

We left early the next morning, having checked out of the hotel and packed our vehicles the night before. We travelled again in convoy, and this time with even more people to a car, as Maryla doesn't drive. I'd luckily managed to procure more petrol through the Maitre D, at a shockingly inflated price, and it was brought to the Duesenburg during the evening, in bottles and canisters, as though it may have been siphoned from another car. I didn't ask questions as to its origins.

CHAPTER 11

Journey to Lwow

Looking back, we were pretty naïve about Hitler's plans for Poland, and the deal he must have done with Stalin. I can barely remember how positive we were as we set out from Naleczow towards Lwow. We thought we could find a safe haven there, and soon return to Krakow. We thought we would be protected under Polish law, with the Polish army defending us, and we thought that we Jews would be able to use our papers without being arrested, bullied, beaten, deported or lined up against a wall and shot. We had a little money, and we weren't hungry. We had three cars, and enough fuel to drive perhaps 200 miles east. We assumed that the Germans and Russians would clash when they met, because Russia must be supporting Poland against the Nazis, and that within a short time, both aggressors would move on to other battles and leave us to get on with our lives. Nobody talked about long-term occupation, or labour camps, or the theft of all our property. Paul, Ania and I were together as a family unit, for the first time in years, and the younger children were safe with us. I didn't feel I had to worry about Tomasz and Max in London, because Britain was not heavily involved, and, being an island, was well protected.

Maryla and her children were under our protection and Olek, if he knew they were in our care, would be greatly relieved. Maryla had written to him from Naleczow, but the post office didn't expect to be able to get letters through to Danzig of all places, so she just had to hope that he would surmise that she was safe and could be reached once we had found a way to call or send a telegraph.

I wondered if there would be a letter from Otto lying on the mat in the Krakow apartment, awaiting my return, recommending our next steps. It was not likely. His regiment must be on the move, and if he was still with them, he might be on the Eastern Front. In any event, he was unlikely to have found any way to send a letter. In my most optimistic fantasy, he had managed to obtain travel visas for us to join him in Rumania or Hungary, and he would be heading home to fetch us. But in my heart I knew he wouldn't have been able to do anything like that, even if he had been as driven as Olek was to try. He could not get into Poland now, I was sure, and besides, even if he reached Krakow by some miracle, we would not be easily followed to Naleczow and then Lwow, across enemy lines. We were determined to lay a trail for anyone trying to find us, and we left forwarding addresses with the hotel and some friends before we left. I could only hope that the war would end quickly with Russia defeating Germany and giving Poland back to us, so that we could get back to normal before Christmas. Somehow, I doubted this could happen. I doubted that Russia had Poland's best interests at heart, and I wasn't even sure that the massive Russian army would be a match for the German war machine anyway. All my plans to travel to England had begun to evapourate as we drove slowly out of the spa town towards to main road east.

As we passed through Lublin towards Lwow, we overtook an endless stream of refugees on foot, also headed in the same direction. Lublin was full of confusion and anger. People were spilling out onto the streets from their houses, carrying beds and chairs, and loading carts and trucks and cars. Children ran across the road in front of us, and their parents kicked at the bumpers when we continued to move forward, even at a snail's pace. The police were trying to direct traffic and shouting at everyone, and it took over an hour to drive the three miles across town. By the time we reached open country on the Lwow side of Lublin, the number of cars on the main road had dwindled, and the majority of those travelling east were families walking, pulling their belongings on hand carts, carrying children on their backs and in many cases, herding a few animals.

After about an hour, driving slowly alongside the procession of carts, we heard the distant roar of engines from the direction we have come.

Isidor stopped his car ahead of us and got out. He turned to face us and looked up, shielding his eyes against the sun. Suddenly he began to wave frantically for us to get out of our cars and off the road. He was shouting over the deafening sound, "Get out, get down, quickly!"

I leapt out and turned to see three distant specks in the sky coming directly towards us and realized in that moment that these must be German fighter planes coming to drop bombs or fire machine guns at us. The children had all climbed out to look, and we had just seconds to grab one another's hands and jump into the ditch beside the road. The planes flew directly in line with the road, lower and lower, until they seemed to skim the treetops, and began firing indiscriminately at the people who were trying to climb off carts and jump into the field across the ditch. There were flashes of yellow and orange light from the wings of each plane, and dust sprayed up from the road in a straight line past us. As the planes passed overhead, I saw an old lady about a hundred yards ahead, who had just clambered down from a cart, simply fold over and collapse by the side of her horse. Then a small child appeared from beyond her, running away from us down the middle of the road with its arms wide open, wailing for its mother. It seemed to leap into the air, as though diving into water, before landing splayed and motionless on the road. As quickly as they had arrived, the planes disappeared towards Lwow, rising into the clouds, and the noise faded. We lay still until the sound of their engines could no longer be heard, and then stood helplessly by the car, staring after them.

People returned from the ditches and fields. Parents called their children and they climbed back into their vehicles. Nobody spoke about what had just happened. I couldn't take my eyes off the corpse of the small child, left untouched for some endless moments. I couldn't see the child's face and had no idea if it was a boy or girl. It just looked like a small pile of clothes, dropped by a passer-by. As I edged the car forward, and it approached the place where the child had fallen, I saw a young mother drop to her knees and pull the child's body into her lap. The blood left a small black pool on the road, which caught the light as we passed. It could so easily have been Anna on the road, and me holding her small body. I turned to look at her and Aneta, as they crouched between the front and back seats, on the floor, paralysed with fear. I placed a hand on Anna's head to try and calm her. I wondered if they had seen what I had seen.

We had no choice but to keep moving. Everyone had returned to their cars and reclaimed their carts and were moving forward at the same pace as before. This cannot have been the first attack they had experienced, and it soon became apparent that it was a regular occurrence in this area. The road was damaged in many places by shells, and all afternoon, the terrible sound of approaching fighters punctuated our slow journey. They were returning every half hour and flying low enough to strafe the walking refugees, and to drop bombs on any trucks carrying Polish soldiers. We were driving extremely carefully and having to swerve around the craters and potholes all the time. Every time the walking people heard the distant engines of the planes, they ran for the fields and lay face down in the mud, hoping to avoid being targeted. Because we were in cars, they heard the planes before us and we took our cue from them. Each time the planes came, they fired on stragglers who couldn't make it across the ditch, and they were mown down where they stood. Several times, we abandoned the cars and joined everyone in the furrows, returning to our vehicles once the planes had passed, checking each other to make sure nobody had been injured. Every time we witnessed the random the deaths of these innocent refugees, it was the same numbing experience, again and again. Every time we returned to the cars, Maryla ran over to hold Aneta and Szymon, before returning to her place. Not once did we stop to help with the bodies, even when someone lay across the road and we had to drive into the field to avoid them. Something prevented us. We had to keep moving, to reach our destination. We had to save ourselves. It had all changed so fast, from a monotonous journey into a desperate cat and mouse escape without the chance of running or hiding. Though we all managed to escape the bullets, and suffered no more than cuts and bruises, the cars all received damage, but thankfully none had its fuel tank hit, though we passed two or three vehicles on fire as we drove.

During what should have been a four-hour journey, but which took nearly ten, we had to leave the road and drive into the adjoining fields many times to circumvent craters, and it was only then that I really appreciated the hardiness of the car, which never once stalled.

Each time we stopped because of planes, when we saw people jumping from their carts, I left the engine running, shouted instructions to the girls to get out, stand against the side of the car and wait for me and Szymon to hold their hands so we would all be together to take our chances in the fields. As we fell forwards, I would try to lay across the girls, in some vain hope that if the machine gun fire found us, it would kill me and not reach them. Anna whimpered at first, complaining that I was squashing her, but I was in no mood to have anyone weaken, and told her to pull herself together, do as she was told and we would be OK.

We often passed dying animals, lying in pools of their own blood, struggling to raise their heads. Enterprising boys with sharp knives could be seen hacking at the corpses of cows or goats and carrying off slabs of meat to keep for their families. When we passed the corpses of old people or children who had not escaped the strafing, I silently prayed that it would not be us next. Why I prayed when I felt so forsaken is something to ask in another life, when peace returns.

In the ditches beside the road were human and animal remains, rotting amongst their broken possessions. I saw bodies half-submerged in the mud, face-down as though searching for buried friends. There was no discrimination in the killing between men, women and children, between cows and horses. Nobody bothered to shoo away the crows, which fed on the carrion, and nobody stopped to bury their dead. Nobody talked as they walked. Nobody answered our questions. They trudged in silence away from Lublin and the invading Germans, towards Lwow and the invading Russians. We knew that we could at any time come against advancing Soviet troops, and we often heard the boom of heavy artillery in the distance ahead of us, so we knew we were heading into fighting.

By late afternoon, we could see a cloud of smoke in the distance, caused by a great fire the which had probably burned for hours. I wondered if it might be Lwow that was burning, and that we were already too late to find safety there. The fighters had not returned for a while and we managed to pull into the side of the road for a few minutes to check on one another. Everyone was equally shocked by what we'd witnessed, and most of us were equally frightened by what lay ahead.

Despite our hopes of Russian allegiance, we were worried about their reputation for violence. Rumours had abounded in Naleczow before we left that on the Ukrainian border the Bolsheviks had burned the villages and raped the women, shot their children and pillaged every property. It was enough to make us all petrified of our own plans to travel east. Perhaps we should turn off the main road and drive up into the mountains, find a village with no name in a remote valley, and a hut to sleep in, and hope to hide when soldiers came. But Isidor and Paul were adamant that we should make for Lwow. They both knew the city well and felt that we would have a far greater chance of survival if we were among large numbers of people, living in relative comfort and security in proper accommodation and gainfully employed to pay for our food, rather than scraping along on what little cash we had brought. Survival. How quickly our circumstances had changed. Not two weeks had passed since we were living in the opulence of the apartment in Krakow, and being served meals by our cook, and just three weeks ago, we'd been ensconced in the Georges Cinq, one of the top hotels in Europe, and Anna had turned her nose up at her food in Gare du Nord.

Our convoy had stopped just twice before in those ten hours, not counting the numerous emergencies. The first time was to allow Maryla out to be sick, which was her reaction to the grotesque scenes we were witnessing, and the second was for the men to get a five-minute break to have some coffee and to relieve themselves behind the cars. Shocked though I would have been had a man done such a thing in my presence before, now it seemed quite inconsequential. Aneta was desperate to go, but couldn't be persuaded to squat by the cars, and ran far out into the field beside us to relieve herself. The endless snaking line of refugees continued past, oblivious to our group, as we stood in the fetid air. And though I tried to ask questions about their destination and origin of one or two women, I got no replies. Everyone's face was a mask of exhaustion, and nobody on foot seemed able to spare the energy to talk. A few cars overtook our vehicles, which we'd pulled in to the side of the road, and it was only when a large truck full of Polish soldiers came towards the cars and would not have been able to pass us without driving into the ditch, that we had to get back into the traffic. While we were stopped this time, I asked Ania how Hugo was coping with the journey.

"He's OK, Miriam. Isidor is remarkably calm and collected and has been cracking his awful jokes and even tried singing songs. But I had to tell him to stop. Frankly I can't stand it when he's so jolly, but it works with Hugo and I suppose it is his way of coping with the stress of driving through this hell. I don't think we will ever be able to forget what we've seen today."

"Do you think we will be in Lwow before nightfall? It is already late and I don't see any signs, unless that smoke in the distance is the city. How far away are we, do you know?"

"Yes, I thought that when I first saw the smoke, but Isidor said it was probably a fuel tank which is well outside the city. Isidor knows the place well and says we have just a few miles to go now. Ada's aunt has a house in the suburbs, and we're going to stop there, so that we can find out how things are in Lwow. She lives alone, and perhaps she will be able to put us up, or at least to recommend suitable accommodation. Isidor has friends who have a large house and they also have a villa in the mountains, so it is possible that they will have left town and we can stay in the house. Ada says her aunt's neighbourhood is accessed through the North gate, but Isidor is expecting every gate to be heavily guarded, and there will be queues to show papers and so forth. They'll probably be looking for German spies who would be scouting the city to see how well fortified it is."

"I do wonder whether we should really be looking for shelter somewhere much smaller, somewhere less important to Hitler's advance, where we might be left alone. Do you think Lwow is not too important, too strategic a centre, and that we will be asking for trouble to base ourselves there?"

"Come on, Miriam, we went through all that a thousand times in Naleczow. Isidor is convinced that the Nazis don't want a show down with the Bolsheviks, and that there will be a settlement between them and a border of sorts. We all agreed that we would rather be subject to a Russian occupation than to be taken prisoner by the Fascists and sent off to a labour camp, only to have our children taken from us and be parted from our men."

Ania looked hard at me, realising how that sounded. "Sorry, Mimi, I didn't mean…"

"That's OK. I'm sure he had good reasons to stay away, and now he probably couldn't return even if he wanted to."

Ania hadn't called me Mimi for years. It was always her nickname for me as a small child, when she would be helping our mother by bathing me, or when we sat at her dressing table as teenagers, and I let her brush my hair for hours while we gossiped about boys. It brought tears to my eyes to hear the diminutive term of affection from her now. Tears that I couldn't shed for all the killing around us, or for the loss of what we had left behind us.

As we approached Lwow, we saw hundreds of Polish soldiers bringing heavy guns into the city, pulled behind trucks and armoured cars. They looked tired but determined and seemed to be digging themselves in to defend the city. Isidor, in the lead car, managed to waylay a captain whom he recognised, who told him that the Germans had already made several air raids on the city over the last two days, and that their ground forces were expected to attack from the hills within the next two. He said that the Russians were not much farther away, on the approaches from Rovno and Tarnopol, and would want to take control of Lwow from the Polish army and defend it against the Nazi onslaught. It was not clear what the Red Army wanted to do, but the captain said that he had orders to defend Lwow against both German and Russian incursions. We would be safe for now in the city, he said, but would be able to go no further, as all the roads to the east were barricaded against the advancing Russians. Isidor thought that the captain was full of bravado for the sake of his men, but that they were not a match for either invading force.

As predicted, we found ourselves in a long tailback of cars and beside them, a much longer queue of families on foot. Many of them had lain down in the dust to sleep, appointing one person to watch over their belongings and to wake them as the queue crept forward. The vehicles were being dealt with quicker, which was probably helped by large bribes being passed from their drivers to the sentries at the checkpoint to speed them through. By the time we reached the gate, the checking of our papers was quite cursory, and because Paul and Ada were able to give the address of Ada's aunt to the sergeant, we were considered bona fides. There were several people being manhandled out of their cars, which were then impounded at the side of the road and stripped of their luggage. One man near us was held at gunpoint while soldiers unloaded crates of alcohol from the boot of his car. It struck me as quite bizarre that even in this mayhem and suffering, there were traders moving into the city with contraband for the black market, and I began a useless mental exercise of counting my Zlotys and wondering what the inflated prices would be like in what was clearly preparation for a siege.

Passing through the ancient arch into Lwow was a huge relief. It wasn't that I loved this city, which I had only been to very occasionally, en route to a ski trip or touring the country, and which I thought ugly and lacking in culture. But I had a sense of being delivered into a citadel, a sense of the protection, which this large and thriving city offered, with its parks and monuments, and the grand architecture. Logically I knew that the gate through which we had passed was no more than a grand entrance around which there was no defensive wall, and that guarding the gate did nothing to stop incursions. I also knew that fine edifices would not stop the bombs and would not ultimately protect us from our fate, but it felt so much safer than the open road, and the stray bullets fired from machine guns in the swooping aircraft we had seen all day.

By the time we arrived into the city centre, the streets were swarming with refugees, and we could go no further. Many roads had been blocked by fallen masonry from buildings struck by the German bombs, some of which still smoldered. I'd never seen the side of a house torn away like this, and it was strangely shocking to look into someone's private life on show in such a way. It looked like the theatre set constructed for some household drama, where the designer wanted the audience to be privy to the intimacy of the actors' lives. The furniture was still to be seen in a bedroom, the bed maybe hanging precariously out over the splintered floorboards and joists. The wallpaper would be intact on some walls, and flapping in the breeze on others, where the brickwork had collapsed but had not torn away the paper with it. In one house, whose front wall had fallen into the street, I could even see a painting still hanging over a delicate French-style dressing table, standing on just three legs. It mattered not whether this was the home of a wealthy family or the cramped quarters of several poverty-stricken families. The bombs made no distinction.

People clambered across the rubble, pulling their possessions from under roof beams or chunks of fallen masonry, or they sat on the stones, dazed and crying for their losses. We crawled by in our comfortable cars, watching the destruction through the windows, as though we were in a cinema. The cars were very low on fuel, and there had been none to buy while we were on the road. Since we'd arrive in Lwow, and passed two or three pumps, it was clear that the city was also out of petrol. The roads were becoming harder to navigate, and we'd have to continue on foot unless we could find somewhere to stop soon. Paul's car was first to stall and we all stopped to discuss moving their luggage into the other cars to keep going, but decided that it was not far now to Ada's aunt Agata's house and that we should abandon the cars and the heaviest luggage long enough to find out if she could take us in, then the men would come back for whatever we couldn't carry now.

We were lucky to have the chance of shelter with Agata, whom I had only met once, at Paul's wedding. We were all loaded down with as many bags as we could carry. I had my portmanteau, with all my valuables in, and Anna pushed her suitcase on a small hand trolley we had brought, so I had only to leave our truck with the clothing, which I thought should be safe, at least for a few hours. Paul led the way and stopped regularly to ask people on the street who looked like locals, for directions. We followed their instructions through the side streets, praying that hers had not been hit by the falling bombs. When we came to a halt outside the dingy terrace, it was a relief to see it hadn't been touched. Paul went to knock, while we sat on our bags, or on the steps, hoping that his aunt would be at home and ready to open the door. After a minute, she shuffled to the door.

Agata was a spinster, a quiet lady in her sixties or older with poor eyesight and a stoop. She was clearly overwhelmed by our unplanned arrival, but pleased to see Ada and Paul, and she let us all in without complaint. With eight adults and four children descending on her, with little food and no bedding, it was obviously going to be too much for us to stay with her in her small home. There seemed to be a tiny sitting room, a parlour designed for one or two people to use, and a scullery with just a gas ring and cupboard beside the sink. Agata had one set of crockery and cutlery, on the draining board, and two pots sitting on the table for cooking. She obviously never entertained, and she had clearly not been out for food in a couple of days and had nothing for the fire either. Paul offered to go and buy a bucket of coal for her and see what was available in the grocery shop on the corner, but Agata told him not to bother, since it only opened for a couple of hours in the morning before everything was sold. Apparently people had to queue in the hope of buying their groceries, only to be turned away once the small amount of produce was gone. We stayed at Agata's house long enough to find out how the city was coping, and where we might look for somewhere to spend the night. We had some tea and we gave Agata what spare food we could, before splitting up to find whatever rooms were available in the neighbourhood.

Agata recommended a friend of hers to me whom she knew was living in a rooming house nearby. The lady, Eva Wojcik, had two rooms on the ground floor of a tall terraced tenement on Arkhypenka Street, which was just a few minutes' walk, and Agata thought that the lady on the top floor had fled only a couple of days ago. Mrs Wojcik had told Agata that the lady's husband had been reported killed on the Western Front, and she couldn't support herself alone. She had gone to live with a sister in Lublin, deciding to take her chances with the German advance.

"She's a Catholic, apparently, so she may be all right. Of course, in Arkhypenka Street, you'll find that most of the neighbours are Jews, and none of them is leaving, but many of the Catholics have chosen the Germans over the Russians and headed west. The area has become more segregated since war was declared, and everyone wants to be among their own. I'm amongst Catholics here, but I prefer to stay where I am. I've lived here since I was a child, you know."

It occurred to me that the people heading to Lublin must have been the few we met on the road, travelling away from Lwow. I had thought once or twice to stop them and tell them what we had heard about the Nazis' advance, but of course they would have had similar tales of the Bolsheviks' advance on Lwow.

I left Anna with her suitcase in Agata's tiny sitting room, where she was now alone with the old lady. Ania and Isidor had opted to drive on to their friends' house on the far side of the city, because Isidor was pretty sure that the house would be vacant since the friends spent every summer at their villa. Paul and Ada opted to walk to the address of another of Agata's contacts from the synagogue whom she thought would put them up in her own home, since they were relatives. I offered Paul the Duesenburg, which still had a little fuel, on condition that he would bring my trunk in the morning, but he refused, because he couldn't be sure how safe the car would be overnight. It would be better, once I'd found somewhere to stay, if I took the trunk into the house, and emptied the car of everything worth keeping. In the event, I wish he'd taken the car, and I was exhausted and would have preferred to leave everything till morning, but it was true that on our drive across the north side of the city, we'd seen cars supported on bricks, stripped of their wheels, with their windows smashed and people sleeping in them.

I promised Anna I would be back soon and asked Agata to let her curl up on the sofa under a blanket while I was out, since she was barely keeping her eyes open. I followed Agata's directions to the house, which turned out to be pretty shabby but at least it was intact. Mrs Wojcik let me in, because the landlady was out. After introductions, she was happy to let me see the room, and felt that the landlady would be fine about it too. I trudged up four flights of stairs to look at a small room under the eaves. It was almost empty, except for an old iron bed, covered in a none too clean mattress, a rickety table and two upright chairs. There was a bucket, a broom and a small cupboard with nothing inside. As far as I could establish, there were no cooking facilities, and no running water. I assumed the landlady provided catering and washing facilities. The small window was cracked, and there was no rug or carpet, just the bare floorboards. I wondered when the old fireplace had last been used, as there was no sign of any fuel or ash. But it was clean enough, and didn't smell of anything except dampness, which was evident in the corner where the roof met the wall, and a gutter was presumably broken. It would have to do for tonight, and then we could look in earnest in the morning for something more comfortable. Surely such a grand city had more genteel suburbs full of small apartments for rent, with furnishings and perhaps the services of a maid or housekeeper. It need be nothing grand or ostentatious, since we had little money to spare, but somewhere adequate. We would, hopefully, hear from Otto soon, and he could probably arrange for a local branch of the Bank of Poland to receive a transfer of funds which we could then live on until this war collapsed.

Eva Wojcik was a quiet and respectable single lady, rather like Ada's aunt Agata in many ways, though perhaps a little younger and certainly healthier looking. She had been living on the ground floor for many years, she said, and the landlady, Mrs Wisniewski, had rooms across the hall from her. She felt sure that Mrs Wisniewski would be happy to rent us the room, and that we should move in tonight, before someone else got to hear about it, and talk to her in the morning, because she would be late back from visiting a sick person in The Jewish Hospital. Mrs Wojcik made it sound as though the hovel in the attic was in fact a great find and that we should consider ourselves very lucky. I didn't want to criticize it, and she was very encouraging about how I might make it more homely, but I had already decided that we would stay not a moment longer here than was absolutely necessary.

I returned to Agata's house to collect Anna, and we drove the Duesenburg over to Arkhypenka Street, rather than lugging our bags on foot. The petrol gauge was already showing empty, but the reliable old beast didn't stall on us. Once we had parked outside, it was then a matter of getting the trunk up four flights of stairs, which neither Anna nor I was capable of. Bit by bit we unpacked the trunk in the car boot and carried our belongings up the stairs to the small room. It took several trips and all I wanted to do then was lay down and sleep. Anna, who is normally oblivious to her surroundings, was shocked when she first saw where we would be staying the night.

"I don't want to sleep in there Mamushu. Look, there's a big stain on the bed, and it's smelly."

"I know darling, I know. But it's just for tonight. We'll find a better place in the morning. Look, you can sleep in your clothes if you're cold, and I'll sleep beside you, so that you will be warm."

By the time we had finished unpacking, and locked the car, the street was empty, and the full moon above us cast an eerie blue light on the houses. We closed the front door and climbed up to our garret, and both fell into the bed without a wash. We were asleep immediately, but in the middle of the night I was woken by shouting from the street far below us and the sound of a window breaking. I would have crept to the window to investigate, but I knew it was painted shut, and I wouldn't have been able to see anything below us. I was so tired that I quickly fell back into a dreamless sleep.

It wasn't until I went down to the yard with the bucket for water in the early morning that I saw the broken glass all over the pavement outside the house and realised that our car had been stolen. I began to fret about its value and how upset Otto would be, and then I decided to let it go. There was no fuel to be had on the open market, the car was a dinosaur anyway, and maybe it would provide shelter for someone living on the street. Otto could rant and rave about it if he ever came to find us. I would miss its opulence, but then Arkhypenka Street was not the right place to park such a grand vehicle. It would have been better to have left it in a smarter neighbourhood, and now we'd have to work out another way to move our belongings to somewhere better. Perhaps cabs still operate, or maybe Mrs Wojcik knows someone with a hand-cart who would deliver for us.

We'd agreed to take breakfast with Agata, and to buy some bread and milk on our way at a bakery she had told us about. It was already eight o'clock by the time I had Anna dressed and washed in the cold water I had carried up the four flights, and we had met the landlady and paid her an exorbitant sum for the room. It was enough for a minimum of a week, which she recommended, and demanded.

"You won't get anything better, Mrs Weiner. There's nowhere to rent, not for love nor money now. You know how many thousands of people we've had coming into Lwow in the last month? And besides, there's plenty of landlords who won't take Jews in, you know. I can rent your room ten times over, and you're lucky I didn't put the sign up in my window, like I was going to this morning."

"And why won't landlords take in Jews, Mrs Wisniewski?"

"Well now, I wouldn't care to speculate, but if you ask me, it's because Jews is being arrested and taken away all over the place. It don't do to be having the police coming into your house and taking people away. It's bad for your reputation, and besides they have no qualms about eating your breakfast off your plate, or stealing your coal while they're ransacking the place. I ask you, what's going to happen if we get over-run by the Hun and that terrible Hitler? Now I'm not prejudiced you know. Some of my best friends is Jewish. I was only visiting Elijah Abramovski last night, who is a lovely Jewish gentleman who was lodging with me for years, and now he's not well and he's in the Jewish Hospital. The place was heaving, mind. Couldn't swing a cat in there, let alone take any more sick people."

"OK, well we must go now or we'll be late. We will see what is available and come back later for our belongings, if we can get a taxi. Did you hear our car being stolen last night, from right under your window?"

"I don't know anything about a car being stolen. This has always been a good neighbourhood you know. I sleep like a log mind, but I do remember a big blue car parked outside when I got home last night. Was that yours?"

Mrs Wisniewski didn't seem at all put out about the theft, and I decided then that her only interest would be in our money and not our welfare. Luckily, our room door had a key, and I had it in my pocket, though probably she had a duplicate and would be into the room as soon as we'd left to see what we had brought with us. I made a mental note to check our belongings when we returned. I carried the portmanteau with me.

The bakery was on the corner of Agata's road, next to the grocers, but there was a long queue already on the pavement and I sent Anna on to tell Agata I would be a while. While I was waiting in the queue, I got talking to the lady in front of me, who was a local.

"Every day I get here earlier, and every day the queue is longer. I've been coming here for years and it's never been like this. The Bidermans who run it are going to have to close down soon, they told me, because they can't guarantee to get the flour every day, and without it, there'll be no baking. It's strictly one loaf each now, if they have any, and I hope you've got plenty of cash, because it's five Zlotys. It was only 50 Groszy a month ago. And just in case you're wondering, they won't take those new Zlotych notes, you know. I don't blame them. It's like toy money."

"We only arrived yesterday, from Naleczow, and we spent the night in a pretty terrible place. I'm wondering whether you might know where we could rent a comfortable apartment in this district, by any chance?"

The lady started to chuckle, and when she saw that I was not joking, she stopped.

"I'm sorry dear. I'm sure that there were plenty of nice places to rent a month ago. Sure, half the city was empty in July, when the rich left for their country summer houses, and all the men joined up, but that was then. Now, if you've a roof over your head, hold on to it and don't let anyone in, because there's an endless queue of people trying to find rooms. You must've seen them, if you came from Lublin yesterday. And they have to stay now because the army has blocked all the roads out. My next-door neighbours have taken two families into their house, as an act of charity, and since word got out, we have people banging on the doors all day long asking if they can come in. Yesterday, someone offered me their gold pocket watch for rent, and someone else pleaded to be my cleaner and housekeeper in exchange for a room."

By then, we had reached the head of the queue, and the lady paid over her five Zlotys and took her loaf of brown bread, thanking the baker's wife and asking after her children. As she turned to go, she smiled sympathetically at me.

"Well, good luck with the house hunting. Perhaps you'll be lucky. I'm sure we'll meet around if you're still in Arkhypenka Street."

CHAPTER 12

Lwow

The day passed quickly, in walking the streets, knocking on doors and asking about apartments. We started in the most expensive suburbs and worked our way down. There was nothing available at any price, and few people even prepared to enter into conversation with us. Some pointed silently to signs in their windows saying "no refugees" or "no Jews", while others simply apologized that they had no space. The lady in the queue had been right. There was nothing to be had, even at prices we couldn't afford. Maryla had managed to find two rooms for herself and the two children, since Szymon, at fourteen, was old enough to be separated from Aneta, who like Anna, shared her mother's bed. She said she'd been lucky to be offered them, and it was only because Olek had a business associate in Lwow, whom Maryla had called on, who knew someone who knew of a place. Their rooms were in a huge old mansion block whose corridors smelt of cabbage and whose front door was always open, since nobody had keys except to their own rooms. We stopped off to see how they were coping, and Maryla had been crying, clearly, as she had puffy red eyes.

"What's upset you? Are the children OK? Did you not sleep last night?"

"Oh Miriam, I just want to go home. This is awful, and I don't know if we can do this. Last night I lay awake, listening to people arguing and doors slamming, and then as I was falling asleep early this morning, someone above us ran a bath and started banging around. The walls are paper thin and the ceilings too."

"Well, at least you have running water in your room, and I'm afraid to say that we no longer have the car since it was stolen in the night."

"Oh God! That's awful. What are we going to do? We can't get out of Lwow when they open the roads unless we have a car."

"I don't think we'll be going anywhere soon, car or no car. I was told today that the Russians are advancing towards our troops, and nobody knows their intentions. They will be here in the next day or two. It seems that they have taken every place they have marched into. Lots of towns have cheered as they arrived, and the Ukrainians and Belarusians are delighted that they are here. We need Stalin to defend the Jews too. Our soldiers are being moved west of the city, to defend us against the Germans, and I heard this morning that Krakow and Lublin have both fallen into Hitler's hands. We were lucky to have left when we did, you know. So we need help here, which might come from France or Britain, but nobody knows if Russia is here to help our soldiers defend the city, or to occupy it and drive out our soldiers."

"Miriam, you're so much better at understanding these political machinations than I am. What about Olek? Do you think he's safe in Danzig? Will he be able to find us here if we stay?"

"I don't know, dear. I know that Danzig is no longer a free state and that Germany has taken over control, but you know how capable Olek is of manoeuvring. If anyone can look after himself, it is your husband. He will find a way to contact us, I am sure. We have left a trail of forwarding addresses, so don't worry. I have more doubts about Otto's safety, and his ability to find us."

"What do you mean, Miriam? Is Otto in danger? Where is he? I thought he was in Bucharest and that he had enlisted."

"Yes, but there is no doubt that the Polish army is in retreat or exile, and that if he sees a battlefield, it won't be one on which he is likely to be a victor."

"Oh dear! We must pray for their wellbeing, along with our own, Miriam."

"You can do the praying for both of us. I have given up."

I left Anna with Aneta for the afternoon and walked over to see Paul and Ada, who had managed to take a room in the house of Agata's friend. Paul was out already, looking for work, and Ada, who is a quiet and quite negative person, I think, was doing her washing and seemed to have settled in well. Paul, who has an engineering background, was thinking about helping with rebuilding homes, or at least surveying the damaged ones, and had apparently gone to City Hall to see if he could talk to the planning department about a job. Ada said she would prefer to stay at home, since her only skill was in secretarial work, and she couldn't earn much, if anything, in that, as she would be competing with locals for those jobs. Ada told me that Isidor had managed to procure some petrol from his friends' housekeeper and had driven over to check on Paul first thing. He said he would be calling to Arkhypenka Street as well, but we must have missed him. Ada said that she thought he had some good contacts in the Mayor's office and that he would be able to find out how and when we might leave Lwow.

On the way back I found a vegetable shop with beetroots for sale and bought some for borscht, and a street vendor who was selling scraps of a carcass he swore was beef, but could have been dog for all I could tell. With these and the remainder of the bread from the morning, we returned to Agata's house because she had a cooking ring and made ourselves and her some supper. She seemed grateful of the company and the news of her friend.

"And how did you get on with Eva Wojcik? Did you meet her upstairs neighbour? She's a lovely woman apparently. I can't recall her name, but she's a Ukrainian. And what did you make of Mrs Wisniewski, the landlady? Eva tells me she's a tough one all right, but fair once she trusts you."

"The less said, the better. I was hoping we'd be moving this evening into more suitable accommodation, but it seems we are too late. Perhaps Isidor will be able to pull some strings for us in time, but for now, I think we must stay put. It's not a place I want to be in cold weather, since there are draughts and the room is damp, and there's no running water in the room. I do so appreciate you letting me use your kitchen, Agata, and I will always be happy to prepare food for you if that's OK with you."

"Of course, my dear. Young Anna needs good hot meals. She's a scrap of a child and needs her nutrition."

We left early in the evening. I didn't want to be out with Anna after dark, and the evenings were closing in. There was a chill in the air when we arrived into Arkhypenka Street, and at the house I was forced to knock for Mrs Wisniewski and to buy a bucket of coal from her which she kept locked in a coal bunker in the back yard. She carefully scooped the lumps one by one into my bucket and made sure that they filled it loosely and no more than to the level of the rim.

Once Anna and I had made a small fire in the grate, we did our best to settle down for the night. There were so many new sounds outside. There were distant explosions and some cries from the street, and there were mice somewhere in the room. Anna fell asleep as I sat over the embers, contemplating our future. It seemed bleak, and insecure, but at least we would be able to share our worries with Paul and Ania, and to make the best of minding Maryla and her children. Lwow wasn't a foreign country, after all, though it was years since I'd been there. The army would protect us and perhaps the Russians would defeat the Nazis. I know that the Bolshevik reputation is atrocious, but perhaps it is true that my enemy's enemy is my friend. For my own peace of mind, I decided to be positive, and to have no expectations.

I was woken early in the morning by the sound of air raid sirens, swiftly followed by explosions. We had nowhere to go for safety, no bomb shelter or cellar, so we had to take our chances. For two days, the city was bombarded from the surrounding hills, and we were unable to go out. We sat in our room, listening in terror as shells rained down and nearby buildings collapsed. We shared what food our neighbours were able to offer us, and we stayed in bed to try and keep warm. Eva Wojcik told me that the air raid warden had called to her, as he knew she was alone, and told her that these were German shells falling on us, and that their forces had surrounded Lwow. The Polish soldiers and volunteers from the city were holding them back. It was a fierce battle, and it wasn't till news came on the third day of the Germans retreating back towards Lublin that we felt able to breathe again. Then we heard cheering in the streets as reinforcements arrived from the east, where our troops had been told to allow the Russians to move forward into Lwow. We thought it might be over, and I decided to slip out to look for food, leaving Anna in our room, with instructions to lock the door. I spent an hour scouring the shops, which were open for supplies, but I wasn't back more than twenty minutes before we were attacked again and the bombing recommenced. Time after time, the houses shook as the bombs struck, and between air raids, there were shells from the hilltops, which smashed into buildings, indiscriminately devastating homes and businesses, roads and churches. We had entered hell, and we had no way out. For five days I didn't see Paul or Ania, and only once received word from Isidor, via a teenage messenger who was looking for payment in bread, that everyone was still safe.

The next morning, we found leaflets scattered on the street, which had been dropped from German warplanes, demanding our surrender. By now, we were confused about the siege and how it would progress. Nothing was clear.

Mr Biderman, who now sold all the bread he could produce, in a few minutes, told me that that the Germans had clashed with Russian soldiers in the hills, and that it was in fact the Russians who were now assaulting the city, using artillery they had confiscated from our own army. We were being bombed with our own bombs! The Polish General, Sikorski, was co-opting able-bodied men and teenage boys from the city to help build barricades, but according to the baker, he had expected the Germans to attack, and the Russians to help defend Lwow. If we couldn't trust Stalin, and the Germans were being kept at bay from the west by all the forces we could muster, it seemed to me that Lwow would soon be overtaken by the Russian army from the east.

After two days of fierce fighting, when Nazi soldiers entered Lwow several times at different points and were driven back by Sikorski's make-shift defense forces, they unexpectedly fell back to Lublin, and a strangely eerie silence fell on the city as we enjoyed a few hours' respite in the fighting. It turned out that the Russian army had approached from the East and had encircled the city and threatened the Polish defenders with an all-out attack. It was clear that this was a vastly larger force, by all accounts up to a million men, and the remaining Polish soldiers and ragbag of refugee volunteers had no hope of defending us. General Sikorski surrendered straight away. The Russian Colonel marched his soldiers right through the centre of Lwow, in a peaceful show of strength, and all the tenants of our house watched from the front window on the stairs, unsure whether we had been liberated or defeated. For all the locals in the Jewish quarter, and we refugees, it was a relief to hear that the Nazis had left us to the Russians, but it wasn't a cause for celebration, as our army was defeated and dejected. Mrs Wojcik recounted stories of Bolshevik atrocities and we listened like fools, as we watched the goings on outside. Crowds stood for many hours on the pavement below our lodgings, at the corner of our road, and watched the disarmed Polish soldiers marching out of the city, under Russian guard. There were injured men on stretchers and others limping with home-made crutches to support them, and there were shuffling, tired and hungry men who were heading out of the city to register with the Soviet administrators before being released to go home. The Polish officers had hoped they would be allowed to leave, but there were apparently a lot of arrests by the NKVD, the Russian secret police, which quickly became our de facto government. Nobody dared ask these police what was happening, but the rumours spread quickly that they had taken over all the police stations and prisons and were incarcerating Polish officers without charge.

Though the city didn't settle back into anything one could call normality, we did manage to sleep through that night, in the silence after the cease-fire. The next day I decided I would have to look for work, as my small amount of money had almost run out. My only training was in secretarial work, which I had studied briefly before my marriage, twenty years ago. The problem was that unless I was prepared to offer my services to our Russian masters, I would not find any demand for administrative work. Their administration would of course all be in Russian, which I had only rudimentary conversational understanding of and I had no knowledge of Cyrillic, so no written Russian at all. Besides, how could I work for an enemy? Why would they employ me, instead of one of their own, or one of the Russian emigres living in Lwow? Paul told me that his contacts in City Hall, Polish government officials, were being demoted or manhandled out of the building by the NKVD officers, and that every department was dominated by Russian or Ukrainian officials.

Most people living in the Jewish quarter were already scavenging for their food, buying it with favours and bartering their small possessions, since Zlotys seemed to have little value. Nobody talked about job opportunities, and even if there were openings, those who heard of them tended to keep the information close to their chests, so they could trade the news, or help place relatives into jobs. I didn't have the contacts that Isidor or even Paul had here, and I didn't want to depend on them to find me something, but I was getting desperate. Our room was freezing at night, even though it was only early October, and we couldn't afford fuel to burn. I had to come up with something else I could do, or we would starve.

Within days of the defeat, we found out that the Bolsheviks were not our saviours, but our lords and masters. Poles were set to work doing the most menial jobs for the NKVD. They would have gangs of starving men breaking rubble and clearing the streets, while the wives were doing their laundry and serving them at table. There were of course worse rumours of sex slavery and rape. The senior officers certainly seemed fairly indifferent about what their juniors did in public, and often in those first days, we saw Russian soldiers either beating up Poles, or jeering and spitting at them. The impression I got was that the invading army was very comfortable with its position in Lwow, and not at all under threat from German or Polish opposition. They had a swagger which pervaded their ranks, and I rarely saw an officer discipline his subordinates, or demand salutes and proper marching even.

On the other hand, this occupying force was made up of the children of Russian revolutionaries and some were old enough to have taken part in the uprising against the ruling classes in Moscow. It seemed strange that since the revolution, the proletariat were not being treated as equals. It was in fact we Jews who were given better treatment than the Catholics, which was because there were so many Russian Jews in the Soviet ranks. At the same time, the Polish Catholic elite who had been running things in Lwow were replaced in their jobs by Ukrainians, who, up to now, had been something of an underclass. Many of the middle-class Catholic government officials were quickly arrested and loaded into trains to be sent to Siberia, and it became known that to be wealthy in Lwow was a dangerous thing. Though I didn't have any dealings with the leaders in the Synagogue, I heard in the neighbourhood that a lot of them initially wanted to work with the Russians, and saw the incursion as a good thing, but they quickly realised that their enthusiasm wasn't reciprocated. The Rabbi in our district was 'interviewed' in the local police station, and though he was later released, that put the elders on notice that they would not be allowed to run the district independently. Meetings between the head of the local NKVD force and the rabbi were public knowledge, and he did not seem to be winning any favours. By then, a lot of Polish Catholics in the city begrudged the Jewish involvement with the Soviets and Jews were being ostracised and even attacked by gangs on the streets for being so supportive of the Russians. It didn't make much sense to me, since Krakow had been a multi-denominational city in which the Jews and Catholics had managed to have a peaceful co-existence for centuries. Of course, there were Jewish districts and Catholic districts there, as there were here, but it had never been this divisive.

Isidor was a sophisticated politician, who was used to manipulating and negotiating for a living. He understood all the machinations of the new balance of power and worked hard to get himself in the centre of things. He had learned to speak fairly fluent Russian, as a diplomat in Warsaw in the thirties, and now he considered it would be appropriate to work his way into a position of power. He had influence with some of the leaders in the Lwow mayor's office and spent his days in and out of City Hall. We saw little of each other, because of the lack of transport in the city, but I did try once or twice to visit him at work in the hope that he could get me some office work there. Each time I asked the receptionist, who was Polish, I was told that he was unavailable, in meetings. On my third visit, I was told that he was no longer working there, though I couldn't get any information as to whether he'd resigned, been sacked, or worse. I meant to go and visit Ania, but it was such a long walk to her house, and even if I made the journey, I couldn't be sure that they would be at home.

The inhabitants of Arkhypenka Street were not close. We kept ourselves to ourselves most of the time and only talked briefly on the stairs, usually to complain about the state of the house, or the lack of facilities. I would be carrying a bucket of cold water upstairs or someone else would be off to buy coal from the landlady, so we rarely got further than a polite greeting. But I started to make more of an effort, for Anna's sake, with the lady who had rooms on the floor beneath mine, the one to whom Agata had referred. She was a lively, strong and energetic young woman named Anastasiya Dabrowski. She had fair hair and a rosy complexion and looked more like a milkmaid than a city dweller. Anka, as she liked to be called, was a Ukrainian Catholic immigrant who had settled in Lwow in the early thirties, and she had indeed been brought up on a farm, and was a Kutak, which she told me meant that her father had refused to pay his dues to Moscow after the revolution. Lenin had called the Kutaks "bloodsuckers, vampires, plunderers of the people and profiteers, who fatten on famine", which she recited to me with pride. Because the Bolsheviks had taken all the farms from the Kutaks for their collective farming programme, her family had been forced to leave their land and travel west in the twenties. She had met Mykola, her husband, in Kostopol, where he was a construction worker. I couldn't see any sign of a man around the house, and I wondered at first whether they had split up.

Anka lived with her three-year-old boy, Wiktor, who was just learning his words, and had a cherubic grin. Anna took a great liking to the boy, who spent most of his time playing alone on the stairs, and she brought him into our room whenever she could and treated him like a doll, cuddling him and singing him nursery rhymes. Anka noticed how Wiktor loved Anna, and she saw that Anna might help her out with the boy, so she began asking us in to her rooms for tea, if she could get some. Wiktor would be under her eye, while Anna played with him, and we could sit at her table because she had four chairs while we only had two. I dared not tell her what life we had left behind in Krakow, in case she thought us to be somehow too posh to keep her company. I needn't have been concerned, since it was obvious we had come from wealth, from our accents, and she could tell by our clothes and Anna's manners. I have never been one to have airs and graces, especially when everyone is brought to the same situation. Despite spending many years relying completely on Celestyna's wonderful cookery, I was not deterred from cooking and sharing our food with a neighbour, especially as Anka had a two-ring cooker. As far as Anka was concerned, we were people in the same circumstances as her and Wiktor, and so we should be treated as equals regardless of where we had come from. In the end, after we got to know one another better, she used to tease me about getting my hands dirty, or when I slipped and fell in the gutter and tore the hem on my dress. But she also respected my education and used to ask for help with form filling, or reading difficult words in a newspaper, without feeling in the least embarrassed.

"So, Anka, tell me about Mykola," I asked innocently over tea. I didn't really know how to open a conversation about her marriage, even though she was a down to earth and open person.

"Miriam, you won't believe me, but he has the hairiest back I have ever seen on a man. He's like a bear with clothing on! He's taller than that doorway, and he often hits his head when he enters the room. He's as strong as an ox and can eat like a horse. I think I must have married a farm animal!" She burst into a bellicose laugh, and I couldn't help myself, but had to join her, even though such conversation would never have been had in Krakow. I'd never had a friend who was so coarse but at the same time so warm and friendly. We'd always been told to avoid loud and uneducated children when we were younger, and as an adult, I had really only ever spent time in 'polite society'. Something had begun to change in me since I came to Lwow, which felt not at all bad, and now I wanted to spend more and more time with Anka because she gave me the hope and confidence I had been losing ever since I left France.

"And, if it's not too rude a question, where is Mykola now?"

"Well, you see, Miriam, I'm not sure. He has been working for the railways for the last year, as a guard on the Warsaw Express, mainly. Anyway, two weeks ago, he left as usual, but he didn't come back. At the beginning I didn't worry, because I know he sometimes stays over a night or two in Warsaw with another guard who puts him up. But now I'm worried that something has happened to him. If there wasn't a direct train back for some reason, he would find an alternative route to return home. I've been to the station to find out, but the station-master told me that the trains to Warsaw were suspended last week, and he had no information about Mykola. He said he would let me know if he heard anything."

"So what are you living on, if he isn't bringing home his wages?"

"Well, not much, Miriam. Wiktor is still breast feeding, though I wish he could be weaned, as his teeth are so sharp, and if I could only get more cow's milk, and oats, I could get him onto solids full-time. I have been working through our pitiful savings, but I'm getting to that point where I'll have to go out to work. I was wondering, whether Anna would be able to help me with Wiktor if I got a job. They seem to get on so well."

Even though it was now only a few weeks since we'd left the comfort of the spa in Naleczow, we had suffered for the drop in our living standards.

Anna and I had both lost weight and being hungry had changed Anna's fussy eating habits completely. She now ate anything that was put in front of her. I was tired and depressed by the dirt and destruction of everything around us, and because it was impossible to keep the place clean. Our clothes needed laundering, and we had only cold water to wash in. Walking to the nearest shop involved climbing over piles of rubble and buying a loaf of bread might involve a scuffle with two or three other shoppers in which the strongest and most aggressive won. I had quickly become hardened to the beggars, and the poor old people I would normally have distributed alms to. Now it was a battle for survival.

"Yes, Anka, I think that would be an excellent idea, and it would give Anna something to do during the day, instead of having her hang around the back yard. I don't want her out on the street, as there are so many people living rough now, and she'd have her clothes stolen off her back in no time."

CHAPTER 13

Work

We were sitting in Anka's rooms, having a bowl of soup, which I had cooked on her gas ring. It seemed a fair exchange, since I had the ingredients, and she the heat.

"What is in this soup, Miriam? It is delicious. I can tell you have turnips and swede, and perhaps some carrot, but is that really bacon I can taste? You should have been a chef!"

"You're too kind, my dear. No such luck. You can taste the end of a Kielbasa Cyganska, which I got off that crook, Nowak, in the grocery shop on Druga Lubienska. It hardly justifies the name of grocery any more, but he seems to have bits and pieces, and I was in there today. I should think it had been hanging in their cellar for weeks, but it is protein and it does add something to the pot, doesn't it?"

"I won't tell the Rabbi, if you won't!" Anka burst out laughing. She was ready to laugh even when all around her were downhearted, and it made her most attractive and rewarding to be with.

"And what did they charge you, if you don't mind my asking?"

"Well, to tell the truth, that greedy pig Nowak was going to have it himself, but he was being berated by The Gorgon for keeping it instead of selling it." The Gorgon was our nickname for Olga, his wife, who towered over him and had been known to beat him in public, according to Anka.

"I could see another fight brewing, so I offered her five Zlotys, but she said the old notes aren't worth having any more, so I managed to placate her by offering to teach their five-year old to read, every day for an hour, while they're in the shop, in exchange for food. Nowak gave me the sausage with the vegetables as a down payment. Unfortunately, their son is rather a stupid boy, and he does snivel a lot when told off, but one can't pick and choose any more."

"Maybe you could take up teaching all the shopkeepers' children and we would all be able to live on your soups!" Anka grinned at me, and Anna laughed for the first time in days.

"I'll have to do something, if the shops will no longer take banknotes. Though God knows I have precious few left anyway. What are we supposed to buy our food with? I need a proper job."

"You and me both. Do you know, Miriam, I haven't seen any of Mykola's wages for three weeks, and that's not funny."

"You've been here longer than we have. Do you know where we could look for work?" Anka was resourceful, and she spent a lot more time than I did talking to people in the street. I still couldn't bring myself to talk with everyone I met. Anyone with resources was out of the city, hiding in the hills in their country houses and living off the land. Everyone in the city spent their time scouring the streets for morsels of information, and blackmarket food.

"There might be work in the soup kitchen on Zadworzanska, down near the park. It's about twenty minutes' walk from here, and apparently it's being supplied by the Russian Orthodox Church, as a gesture of goodwill. The priest has friends in the NKVD apparently, though how any of those bastards... Sorry Anna... would have a religious bone in their bodies is beyond me. The kitchen needs good cooks and people who are ready to stand behind the counter for several hours doling out gruel to the endless queue of starving people. I have a friend there who said she'd get me in to see the manager. But you're a much better cook than I will ever be, and we could go there together to see if they'd take us both. What do you say?"

"Let's go now and see if we can get work is what I say."

It would be a relief to have something simple and repetitive to do, to take my mind off worrying. I was worried about Maryla and her children, who had very little money left, and I was worried about Paul and Ada who were also short of funds, and I hardly saw Ania and Isidor any more since they lived across the city and we had no transport. I worried about the Bolsheviks and their aggressive manner in the streets. They had soldiers patrolling every corner and all the civic buildings, and they regularly beat up men who were living rough, without provocation. I worried about all the people who were being rounded up for deportation or who were apparently rotting in jail, and I worried about Anna, who was pale and sickly, and friendless and uneducated.

Anka and I went that afternoon to see the manager, who was a hard-looking woman named Martyna Kowalewicz. She had been a chef in an hotel before the war and understood how to make the most of her supplies. There was no discussion of our wages, which turned out to be sporadic, but she asked us both how many children we had.

"Bring a covered pot tomorrow, and you can each take home a portion of whatever we're serving for each child and one for yourselves each day. No preferential treatment – you get the same food as the people in the line. You start at 7.30am sharp and we finish when the food runs out or the last person has been served. So that will always be when the food runs out, since the line is endless."

"What are our duties?" Anka asked.

"Whatever I tell you to do. There are five in at the moment, and with you two, that'll make seven. Mrs Weiner, you can be on food prep tomorrow, and Mrs Dabrovski, you'll start on washing up, and once the food is ready to be served, you'll both spend your time serving and clearing tables. Any stealing food and you're out, and I know the local police pretty well, so watch what you do."

"And is there anything we need to know about who to serve?" I wondered if there was any preference for feeding particularly destitute people, or children first.

"You need eyes in the back of your head. There's always people coming back for seconds, if they've nothing better to do than stand in the queue all day, and there's a lot of rough ones who push in, and demand more when you're serving. Stand back so they can't grab you, and see this ladle? Use this for serving – one scoop per person – and to hit anyone who tries anything on. Don't hold back, because if they think you're scared, they will keep at you. The same ones do it every day, and they're pretty hard to deal with. I had to let Eve Novak go last week because she was too good looking."

"What's wrong with being good looking?" I was shocked to hear of such a strange discrimination.

"Single woman. All the men who flirted with her thought they'd get extra food. Not that they got away with it, but she was sweet on one young man, and he brought his friends and they tried to distract me while she passed out extra servings. I saw him hanging around as we closed up, and I just can't spend my time watching the staff. She had to go."

"So what will we be cooking tomorrow? Do you get meat, or is it all vegetables?"

"Whatever it is, you'll find out in the morning, when Antoni comes with the cart from the church. It's mostly donated by Russian Orthodox people who are devout, and I think they get some from the NKVD cook who feeds the guards in Zamarstynowska Street prison. They're the ones who accompany Antoni's cart while he pulls it round here, otherwise he'd be jumped every morning and mugged for his delivery. We sometimes get meat, but don't ask me what it is. I don't want to know, and so long as it isn't crawling with maggots, we'll cook it."

The next morning, Anna and I got up earlier than usual, and washed in the dark. She went down to help Anka get Wiktor up and dressed, while Anka and I got ourselves ready for the walk to Zadworzanska. It was only just getting light and was already frosty. In another month it would be pitch dark at this time, since all the street lamps were out of action, and there would be snow and ice to contend with. But I had my good winter coat which doubled as a blanket at night, and a pair of seal skin boots. Anka didn't seem to feel the cold and this morning she had only a shawl around her bare arms. Everything we wore looked tired and drab, which was just as well, since I had heard about women being stripped of their outer clothes in the streets by teenagers who collected clothing for the street vendors to sell on.

We worked in the refugee kitchen seven days a week, for up to twelve hours a day, cooking and cleaning and serving the people who had walked across the city for a bowl of food. I hadn't worked for twenty years, since my marriage, and now I was slaving away beside Anka, while Anna stayed home to look after Wiktor, and I was still hard pressed to earn enough to feed Anna and myself and to pay the rent. Anka had her own problems. When Mykola didn't come home, she finally heard from the station-master in Lwow that his train had been blown up and he had been killed, along with dozens of passengers. She cried for just a few minutes, and hugged Wiktor till he began to wail, but she didn't mention Mykola to me again from that day.

The soup kitchen provided me and Anna with one meal a day, which I ate during the shift, and she had when I got home at night. She was sick often from the food, which was far from wholesome, and we had very little to supplement it, since the deal I'd struck with the Nowaks fell by the wayside. It was no surprise to me as I was unable to be there when they needed me to look after their little boy during the day, and they didn't really care enough about his ability to read and write to offer me any of their meagre supply of food in exchange for teaching him when I was not working in the kitchen. It became a struggle to buy food without having the means to pay, so we went without. It was hard to imagine the dinner parties in Krakow, with the silverware and Meissen, cut glass decanters and fine wines. How wasteful we used to be when half a chicken was left over, and we'd throw it away, or when we were out so many evenings that expensive food we had purchased was not good enough to use and was given to the dog next door. It was painful to recall that last dinner in Paris which Anna had turned her nose up at, and the plate of cold meats we'd picked at in the kitchen the night we returned home.

CHAPTER 14

Ania and Isidor

Ania has always played the part of the responsible older sister to
me. She thinks she has to protect me because Papa chose to put
me and Paul under the guardianship of Uncle David when we
were children and Mama had passed away. Ania was already older and she
stayed in Papa's house to look after his household, and as a consequence,
she became more of a carer I suppose. When she met Isidor, and they
became engaged, it was a subject of much discussion as to whether they
would take Papa to live with them when they were married or whether
he could manage with a housekeeper. In the event, his heart attack and
quick decline solved their problem before they had to. Isidor would never
have wanted his father-in-law as a dependent. Their son, Hugo, was born
soon after their marriage, and Isidor's political career in the twenties was
quite meteoric. He would have perhaps stood for Parliament, had not war
been imminent, and his frustration at missing out on a seat was quickly
redirected into making money through his political connections. Ania
inherited a share the leather business, and Isidor developed that into an
international brand of handbags and luggage, which was closely tied to my
inheritance in the tanning and wholesaling side of things, which Otto was
responsible for. Because Otto's first experience of business, under Lolek's
tutilage, was timber, and later, with Olek, furniture, he had little interest in
the leather business. As a consequence, without careful handling, it became
something of a financial liability. Isidor strongly disapproved of Otto's
disinterest, and especially as he had been buying all his leather from Otto at
the beginning. This created unnecessary tensions between Isidor and Otto,
which in turn affected my relationship with Ania. Her need to care for me
was tempered by her need to use me to push Otto over his handling of

the tanneries. Otto and I had learned early in our marriage not to discuss business except in his telling me anecdotes about the staff, or about his day at work, and I agreed never to challenge him on his business decisions. When Ania asked me to have a word with Otto, I always refused, and she became enraged.

"Papa would be turning in his grave if he knew what a mess Otto is making of your inheritance, Mimi. I really cannot understand why you don't insist on Otto taking more interest in the business. We could do so much more as a family you know."

"Ania, I love you dearly, but I must ask you not to get me involved in what is a discussion that Isidor should be having directly with my husband. You may be the power behind the throne in your household, but you know that Otto doesn't like me to interfere in his business affairs, and frankly I don't want to be involved, either."

"We've always stood by you and Otto, and Isidor has always been loyal to the family, even when the quality and price of leather is better from other suppliers. I don't want to let this come between us, and certainly it isn't my place to come between you and Otto, but please don't stand by and let the business collapse."

"Ania, I think, in future, we should not discuss business at all. If you can't manage that, please don't come to me with Isidor's problems."

As time went on, Isidor started to buy very well from a Ukrainian supplier, who helped him with connections in Moscow, and by the mid-thirties, he and Ania had a very smart outlet in the centre of Moscow and travelled regularly there. They were very wealthy, and Isidor began to win contracts to make leather products for the Russian and Polish armies; saddles and panier bags and weapon cases and suchlike. As his business grew, Isidor needed a local supply of leather he could depend on, and he offered to buy me and Otto out of the tanneries, and Otto agreed, because the price was right. Once that had happened, relations with both of them became much easier, and we began to socialize more regularly, so long as everyone adhered to the unspoken agreement not to talk about the state of the tanneries which they had acquired.

When war looked likely, Isidor pushed hard for more military contracts, but as soon as Russia invaded Poland, the Government insisted he cut all his ties with Moscow, and he was unable to get his money out. As we travelled from Krakow to Naleczow, and then to Lwow, Isidor was still hoping he could negotiate his way into the Russian army contracts, which had been suspended, without being challenged, since the Polish government had gone into exile and were not in a position to enforce their demands. It was a dangerous game he was playing, and I was sure that he would fall foul of one or the other side. When he found a way to work in Lwow City Hall, it was in the procurement department, in which he knew he could not only negotiate preferential deals for his own business, but also take a cut on any other supply contract that he was responsible for negotiating. In fact, while he was unable to contact his Ukrainian leather supplier direct, he developed some contacts in the NKVD who were able to do so for a fee. Also, once he had his feet under the table, he found that there were channels of communication with the German administration in Krakow, albeit slow and unreliable. Though we never talked about it directly, it was apparent that he was continuing to run parts of his business from Lwow. I was quite concerned when I found out that he was no longer in City Hall, and it transpired that he had finally come under the scrutiny of the head of the Russian administration, who was an accountant and clearly enjoyed teasing out any 'leakage' in the finances. The deal between Moscow and Berlin over the partition of Poland was founded on trade. Russia was expected to deliver huge quantities of supplies and equipment to Hitler, and the strain of the deal was all placed on cities like Lwow to come up with their share of provisions. Isidor's commission was considered an unacceptable cost, given his nationality and religion, and he was pushed out. If he hadn't been so well connected, he would have been deported to Siberia for wheeler dealing, but he managed to call in favours with Moscow to have his punishment commuted to sacking, on condition that he relinquish all his contracts with Russia to his Ukrainian supplier, who felt he could service the army's needs without Isidor's help. The issue of Isidor's Moscow bank accounts was never mentioned, since he couldn't afford to let the NKVD know how much money he had in Russia, because they would simply confiscate it.

Ania and Isidor came to visit at Christmas, and brought a bottle of Krupnik, which Isidor had been given by someone in the City Hall whom he kept in touch with. It was the first alcohol I'd tasted in four months, and it was remarkably invigorating. I understood after one small glass how people living on the street would prefer to spend their few Zlotys or barter their trinkets for home-made spirits, and risk blindness, rather than buying food. Since November, we had been seeing dead bodies in the streets nearly every morning on our way to work, because people sleeping out were subjected to sub-zero temperatures with no protection. Men would get dead drunk on potato gin, and fall asleep without bothering to cover themselves properly, and would be frozen solid by morning.

It had snowed throughout early December and even during the day, temperatures rarely rose above zero. Nobody tried to remove the frozen corpses or to dig the hard ground to make graves, and we quickly became inured to the sight.

Anna spent almost all day with Wiktor, under the bed covers, and we only had fuel for occasional fires in the evening, so usually I went to bed after returning home. Tonight, we had a coal fire, because Isidor had paid Mrs Wisniewski an eye-watering twenty Zlotys for a bucket of coal when they arrived. She saw him coming and fleeced him for twice the price she normally charged, but Isidor didn't argue. He clearly still had plenty of reserve funds.

"It's lovely to see you, Ania. How have you been?" I thought Ania looked drawn and tired, but otherwise she hadn't lost weight as much as most people. She and Isidor were probably still eating well enough.

"I'm fine. How about you? Poor Anna looks so pale, and she's as thin as a rake. Are you getting enough to eat?" Anna had gone down to Anka's rooms to play with Wiktor, and to give us some privacy.

"She's not very well, to be honest. She is sick and has diarrhoea every day. I bring her a bowl of whatever we make in the kitchen when I come home at night, but by then, it has been standing all day, and the food we have been getting from the Russian priest is none too fresh in the first place. She sometimes finds it hard to keep down, and I think she may have had some food poisoning. She clearly has some form of dysentery but of course there's no doctor near here. I've been thinking of selling my pearls to buy medicine, but I need to find someone with the right supplies and to get their price before I do that."

"If we can help, we will. I'll ask my neighbour, who knows all the best people, to get in touch with you." Ania was silent, and looked hard at Isidor, whom she clearly expected to say something. He coughed and looked steadily at me.

"Miriam, we wanted to talk to you about the future. You know that I was forced out of City Hall last month, and that there are a number of people who would like to see me deported. We've decided to move on. We're planning to try and get out of the country. I have heard news of the NKVD's plans for a wholesale arrest of Jews who are politically connected, which would include those of us who have worked in Warsaw and so on. Despite my ties with Moscow, I can no longer access the NKVD's internal mail system, so I can't lobby for support in the right places. I'm certain to be on the list, because of my ties to the Mayor who was removed last month. They will undoubtedly send those whom they pick up to Siberia, or they will execute them in the local prison yards."

"My God, Isidor, I didn't realise it could be so dangerous here for you. You seem always to keep ahead of the dangers, and I never thought you would also be a target for those awful Bolshevik killers."

"You shouldn't worry, I'm used to people chasing after me. It's one of the hazards of the job in my walk of life."

"So you're planning to leave? Surely that's enormously risky. What do you think, Ania?"

Isidor always made irrevocable decisions and Ania, though she was a strong enough person, never went against him. Once he had lost his job at City Hall, to a cousin of the head of the NKVD in Lwow, and he heard about the lists being drawn up of prominent Jews sought for deportation, Isidor felt he had no choice.

"What have you been doing since you lost your job, Isidor?"

"I haven't been out much. I'm convinced that the house is being watched, and it's only a matter of time. Besides my own safety, I'm concerned that we will all run out of food if we stay here. They haven't closed the gates to the west, so the refugees keep pouring into town, but the Russians are confiscating food to supply their soldiers, and we will all starve before the spring, unless we can get access to fresh farm produce. Frankly, I'm amazed your kitchen is still getting food."

"It seems that some well-connected people in the Russian Orthodox church receive food direct from the NKVD, who are confiscating it from the surrounding farms. They are put under pressure by the priest to donate a portion of their bounty to the church, who supply us each morning. But you're right, the quality and quantity of food we're getting is dropping, as quickly as the number of people queuing for it is increasing. Some of them are just coming into the soup kitchen to feel warm for a few minutes, and even when we run out for the day, they want us to keep the place open, rather than heading back out to the street. We have to threaten to have people thrown out after they've eaten."

"Miriam, I have enough money to bring you with us, and Ania and I would like you and Anna to consider coming. It isn't going to be easy, but we feel it will be safer than staying. Anna will have a much better chance of regaining her health in a warmer climate. We have every chance of making it to Palestine, and if not there, then perhaps Morocco or Algeria. I hear that Jews are not mistreated in North Africa."

"Thank you Isidor, but I am not sure Anna is fit to travel, and besides, we haven't any travel permits. How will you make it across the border, even if you can get on a train? You say you are somebody that the Bolsheviks would love to arrest, and I would imagine that bribes would have to be substantial for them to let you though their cordon."

"I have made arrangements, and we have procured travel papers for the train. I am someone who has simply done his job, and not a spy or an agent provocateur. I have been in touch with some of my colleagues in Chernovtsy, and they say that it is still possible to travel through Rumania without the careful checking that goes on here. That means finding a border crossing which is possible, and I'm sure we will make it. Trust me, Miriam, I would not put us all at risk."

I hadn't thought about leaving, as it would have been impossible for me to organise papers. Even now, I wasn't sure if Isidor meant that he could procure good travel permits for me and Anna, or if he simply planned to buy our freedom. He was always a gambler, and it was usually only his own safety and perhaps Ania's he was gambling with. Now I was being offered a chance to gamble, and Isidor was going to be placing the chips. I trusted him to a point, but I have always found him to be too much of a risk-taker and prepared to rely on his brazen approach to winning. It seemed to me that for Anna and me, the risks were too great, and even though I would be heart-broken to see them go, I couldn't risk our lives with his and Ania's. We had no choice but to stay where we were not going to be picked up by the Nazis and sent to labour camps. To my mind, Lwow was safer than Hungary, even though The People's Commissariat, which ran several prisons in the city was forever arresting Poles for political crimes against communism. They didn't seem to be anti-Semitic, but Isidor was bound to be much more unsafe here than we were. He certainly had a public face and his pre-war role in Polish politics, not to mention his manipulations and dealings at City Hall, made him an obvious target. Since he'd lost his job and was in hiding, Ania hadn't been able to work, as I had, because everywhere that offered legitimate employment had been forced to check papers and record employees' details, which the NKVD reviewed very regularly against whatever records they had of 'people of interest'. Ania had taken Isidor's name, rather than keeping her maiden name, and so even if she worked and he hid out in their house, it would lead them to him.

I sat staring into the fire, while Isidor poured another shot of the fire water. Ania reached out and took my hand.

"Please, Mimi, for Anna's sake."

"I have to say that I feel safer here, since we have a place to sleep, and I have work, and for myself and Anna, we aren't likely to be of interest to the NKVD, in the same way as you are, Isidor, and in my view we have to just wait it out. What do you think, Ania?"

"I understand your feelings, but I think Isidor is right. We can't keep going on our savings. I've already sold most of my jewelry and the cash we brought with us is buying nothing any more. It's different for you, because you have work, but since the problems at City Hall, Isidor can't show his face, for fear of being picked up. We have to move on. I know it's risky, and I fully understand your worries about little Anna. Perhaps, if we make it to Chernovtsy OK, and we can get word to you about the best way to come, you'll join us?"

"I'll follow if it is safe, of course, and if I can get papers. When are you planning to leave, Isidor?"

Isidor looked across at Ania and then back at me.

"It has to be tomorrow, Miriam. My contacts can only help us straight away, before their orders to arrest me are handed down officially. Besides, so many good people are being replaced by NKVD, and the security of the railways is an obvious priority."

"Oh God. So soon! I won't know what to do without you nearby, Ania. Paul and Ada will be devastated too, but you and I have always had each other to lean on."

We both cried then, which is something I never did. I wondered if I'd ever see them again. If I'd been in any way a believer, I'd have prayed for them fervently, day and night. But who could believe in a God that watched Hitler and Stalin's behaviour, without stopping the destruction?

CHAPTER 15

Valuables

It's true that Isidor is very resourceful and Ania was always less ready to get her hands dirty than I, but even their finances had run low, and the journey they planned would take what they had left, in bribes. Isidor prepared their journey to Chernovtsy with meticulous care, and he promised to try and find Otto's regiment once they reached Rumania, which was an unlikely prospect. I gave him a letter for Otto but didn't expect it would ever be delivered. A lot of Jews were making their way across the Black Sea to Palestine, and Isidor's plan might work, if Turkey would let them through. I would perhaps have travelled with them, but Anna was too unwell, and we had to stay.

At the beginning of our stay in Lwow, when the Germans were still bombarding the city, Paul had volunteered for a gang of workers, which had the dangerous and unsavoury task of going into damaged buildings each morning after a night of bombings to help clear rubble and search for bodies. He'd first tried at City Hall to get work as a structural engineer, since that had been his work in Krakow, and had only been offered manual work. At least he could make use of his knowledge when risking his life and that of his workmates entering dangerous buildings, and when planning how to shore up walls. After the fighting stopped, his main job was to try and repair any houses that were not too badly damaged and move families off the streets into them before they froze to death. There were about 300,000 Jewish refugees in Lwow by that second summer, and already every possible place was fit to burst. Our own house had two new families living in the rooms across from Mrs Wojcik, as the landlady had moved in with her sister, so she could earn more rent. Although it was cramped, everyone made the best of their circumstances and we shared what work we could do around the place. The back yard was a play area for all the children in the house, especially as the coalbunker had been empty since February.

We saw what we could of Maryla and the children, who still received a small income from Olek, but I felt that once Ania and Isidor had gone, Paul and Ada were my only family in Lwow so we met up every week if we could. Maryla didn't work, so she would happily mind Anna and Wiktor if need be, while I worked.

Paul managed to feed himself and Ada from the donations people made for his help with their houses, or when they had been saved from the streets and could find something to give him. But it was a hand-to-mouth existence, which we came to accept, and even to cherish at times. Everyone we met was intent only on survival and few people in the city were prepared to abuse one other's generosity, when the aggressors were always there, ready to arrest trouble-makers, beating or even executing anyone they wanted, without retribution. We felt part of a community of sorts. People had real problems, real lives to live. They weren't concerned about the colour of the curtain fabric in their houses or the shine on their silverware. Choosing what to have for dinner was no longer an issue, and as for clothes shopping, it never entered our heads any more. We were coping and we were helping one another, and in some strange way, I felt freer than I had in twenty years. Anka was a rock for me to hold on to. We talked all the way to the soup kitchen in the mornings and all the way home, however tired we were. We could look out for one another if either of us was accosted by some threatening street urchins or a pushy NKVD guard looking for trouble. Neither of us was young or beautiful, and we had long since stopped looking elegant or well dressed, but the Russian soldiers were obviously living in cramped conditions with only male company, and the street patrols were always looking for women's attention.

"OK Ladies, let me see your papers."

We met these same two policeman every other day on the same corner, and they always asked to see our papers, in order to waylay us.

"Miriam Weiner. Married, heh? Nice photograph. Where are you going?"

"Home, the same as every other time you've stopped us on this corner."

"Looks to me like you're out on the prowl. Have you been shop-lifting?"

"Shop-lifting? Oh for goodness sake, there's nothing to steal in the shops, and even if there were, where would I conceal stolen goods? I don't even have a handbag anymore."

"Ah well, plenty of places to hide a salami, if you want. Know what I mean? Can't be too careful with you lot. What are you carrying under your shawl? I think we'd better search you." The two men tried to shove me towards the alley, but Anka, who was substantially larger than me stepped between them and me.

"Look, sargeant," she said "we're on our way home. We've just worked 12 hours in the soup kitchen on Zadworzanska, and we're tired. You know us. You check our papers every week. She only has a bowl of soup for her sick child, and I have nothing. But if you insist on checking, let's go to see Inspector Mikhailov. We're only around the corner from the station. He can supervise the search. You're Sargeant Petrov aren't you? He mentioned you to me last time we met."

The inspector was often in to see Martyna Kowalewicz, to make sure that his boys at the police station were getting their share of donated food from the church. It was an awful compromise to be running the kitchen on donations, which had to be shared with the NKVD in exchange for our permission to feed the starving refugees. Since Anka was now the only member of staff who was single, and younger than the rest of us, Mikhailov had shown a lot of interest in her. While she kept him at arm's length, she was prepared to chat to him when he attended to her, in order to smooth the way for Martyna's negotiations, which in turn would keep our jobs secure. Knowing an inspector had its value.

"All right. Move along then." The guard and his friend pretended to be unconcerned about Anka's name-dropping, as they turned and strolled off to the corner to look for someone else to harass.

I'd heard nothing from Otto, and what little cash I had retrieved from the apartment in Krakow had long been spent. I had no access to our bank accounts, and even if I had had, it is likely that the money was gone. Isidor had told me in December that all the Jews he knew in Lwow who had bank savings when they arrived had found their accounts had been closed and their savings confiscated. It seemed likely that if Otto had managed to access our own savings from some Rumanian bank, he would have taken out what he could and was presumably holding on to it in Reichsmarks or buying gold. The Zloty was pretty well worthless and the exchange rate was punitive, as Germany wanted to pillage Poland's wealth and have it transferred to its coffers. Ania had sold all her jewellery in the autumn, presumably to help pay for their travel papers, and she'd suggested to me that I trade what items I had so far managed to hold on to for Reichsmarks, or Roubles. The German currency was now being accepted by shops and street traders in preference to Zlotys, even though we were still governed by Soviets, but I couldn't bring myself to do it. I had considered selling individual items when we needed medicine or when the rent was due, but nobody was going to offer refugees a reasonable price on such valuable pieces. Ania hadn't managed to find a doctor for Anna before they left, so I had done my best to keep her well, without medication. Her problems were the same for half the population: poor sanitation, rotten food and lack of clean water or fresh air, and there was little to be done.

I decided to hide my two necklaces, the pearl earrings and my diamond ring, rather than sell them. The city was full of thieves, and it was becoming dangerous to go out after dark. The police were not to be trusted, and we were surrounded by so much violence. Every day someone was murdered in a back alley over a debt or as a possible informer, and we were all terrified of being reported to the authorities for anything at all.

One morning, I met Anka on the stairs, so we could walk together to the kitchens for our 7.30 start, and she was quite agitated.

"What's the problem? You look shaken." I had become very attuned to Anka's state of mind, since Mykola had gone, and her positivity was like a drug for me. Without it, I found every moment of the day much harder to manage.

"Did you not hear that Mrs Wojcik was robbed at knifepoint of her watch and purse in the doorway, last evening, when she was coming back from work?"

Eva Wojcik still worked in a small clothing factory she'd been with since the '20s. Since war broke out, they had been making uniforms and flags, and now they had contracts with the Russians for shirts. She was as quiet as a mouse and always refused to join Anka and me when we were sitting together over tea. I had tried several times to engage her in conversation but she always greeted me with a shy smile and disappeared into her room before I could stop her.

"Oh no! Was she hurt? Who was it, do you know?"

"No idea. You know how she is. I couldn't get any information out of her, and I only heard about it from Mrs Wisniewski, who came around this morning with that man she's hired to protect her money, when I was handing over the rent. I can't help thinking what would have happened if the thieves had pushed past Mrs Wojcik into the house and been up the stairs to murder us in our beds?"

I had long since stopped wearing my diamond engagement ring and had been leaving it in my portmanteau under the bed in our room, but anyone who could pick a lock or who chose to break in would take the case, which itself was saleable, not to mention its contents. Also, if we had to move on in a hurry, which was often on my mind, I might not be able to retrieve it.

Before they left, Ania had introduced me to a dentist neighbour of theirs in the smart suburb where they lived. He had done some fillings for Isidor, and he told Ania that he had a side business going, helping anyone with diamonds to secrete them in their teeth. When we met, I was wearing my engagement ring, and as soon as he saw it, he offered to implant the stone in a molar for me. It was a big diamond, and he said that it would be a difficult task, but it would be possible to leave enough of the tooth to disguise it.

After the story about Mrs Wojcik, I decided to make the journey to his surgery with the ring. I had managed to scrape together the money to pay him to operate, and he pulled the tooth while I was unconscious from a breath of ether, drilled it hollow and hid the diamond before re-implanting it in my mouth. The platinum setting I sold to him for scrap, since he seemed eminently more trustworthy than the street traders in our neighbourhood, and he was clearly dealing with wealthy people who wanted to convert their cash and cars into precious metals so that they could carry their wealth around, stitched into their clothing. With the proceeds of the platinum, I bought some tonic for Anna. Painful though it was to have a tooth out, I knew how important it was to protect heirlooms. One day, Tomasz would marry and would give his wife my diamond.

CHAPTER 16

Maryla

Over these few months, while life still had some sort of routine about it, Maryla, Szymon and Ancta managed to survive on the money she received from Olek. It hadn't been possible to send money to her by mail, but she received regular visits from Conrad Brzozowski, a friend of Olek's who was often in Lwow on diplomatic business. Szymon was fourteen and able to help Paul in his work, and to share in some of the food parcels given to Paul as gifts that he and Ada were living on, so Maryla and the children usually had food. She shared what she could of her income with me, but Olek's friend wasn't able to help the rest of us directly, though we did have high hopes at the beginning for Conrad to help us all keep in touch with the outside world. He had, apparently, been involved in diplomatic relations between Hungary and the Polish government before war broke out, and he had so far managed to use his old diplomatic papers to travel between Lwow, where his family was, and Danzig, where he and Olek met regularly. Though Olek had asked him in October to try and find Maryla, it wasn't until Christmas that he found her in Lwow, having been to the Naleczow spa, at Olek's behest. We had left the address of Agata with the spa hotel's manager, the only forwarding address we had, in case Otto or Olek was able to get into the country. Eventually, on his Christmas trip to see his mother in Lwow, Brzozowski looked Agata up and found out about Maryla's whereabouts. After that, whenever he travelled to Danzig, he was able to update Olek with the news Maryla gave him, and to bring her money. I would have liked to meet Conrad, perhaps to talk to him about finding Otto, or to ask about Ania and Isidor's possible whereabouts, but he never announce his arrival in advance, and I was always at work when he visited Maryla.

After he'd been, she would come to see me with Olek's news, which was usually in the form of a letter he had written to her. Sometimes it was hard to know what he meant in his comments, which were clearly written so as to be indecipherable to others, should Conrad have them confiscated. Olek was managing without any work, and clearly had very little to live on. The timber business had all but ground to a halt, and he was forced to flee Danzig because of his Jewish blood. He'd based himself in Bucharest for the last few months, but was moving around quite a lot, as far as we could tell. He only mentioned Otto once or twice. Otto had been in touch from Hungary to say that his regiment was being disbanded and most of his cronies were heading to Scotland to serve in the Polish Free Army there. Otto was going to try and reach Bucharest, rather than heading to Scotland, and he would then work with Olek to try and get us all out of Poland. Maryla and I discussed our prospects of escaping Lwow and neither of us gave this much credence since Jews were just not getting travel permits any more. Olek had some sort of diplomatic status himself and had far more chance than Otto of helping Maryla, though she had little encouragement from Conrad about travelling. He would have to play his part in bringing visas to travel, and he didn't think it likely that Olek could buy them.

In order to obtain visas, Olek finally returned to Danzig under false papers, because he had a good contact who would prepare them for Maryla. They must have cost him something very precious, since Danzig was not a city in which Jews were offered legitimate travel papers. Just when Maryla and the children were really struggling to buy food or manage on Paul's diminishing provisions, and she was beginning to despair, he managed to send some travel visas to them with Conrad.

In the same way as Isidor and Ania had appeared and broken their news to me, Maryla came to see me one evening, and they left the next morning on a train to Budapest where Olek could meet them. Brzozowski's trips to Danzig from Lwow didn't last much longer. Paul found out through his boss at Lwow City Hall that he was deported to a Siberian labour camp before the year was out. In the hope of reaching Otto, I often left letters with Maryla for Conrad to deliver, so that she could give them to him for Olek. I had no idea whether Olek and Otto were in regular contact, and whether Otto was also traveling to Danzig. Unless he'd found money, or work, it seemed unlikely, and he could have moved from Budapest months ago for all I knew. If he had managed to visit Olek, or crossed into Danzig, and he could source visas as Olek had done, then Brzozowski might be able to do for Anna and me what he had done for Maryla. It was one of those convoluted day-dreams I had, until Maryla left and it began to sound like a useless fantasy. After she'd gone, I heard nothing more of Brzozowski, and though Maryla promised to help Anna and me, if she could, that proved impossible. In fact, after that night when she came to give me her stove and a few other possessions, I never saw Maryla or her children again. It was another wrench, to lose them. It was not the same as it had been with Ania and Isidor, but despite the history, I had become very fond of Maryla and Aneta had continued to be friends with Anna. Szymon looked like Otto as a young man, in the photographs of his teenage years, and he had the same earnestness about him.

In all those months when we met at least once a week in Lwow, I didn't talk to Maryla about Otto, and she never asked me how I felt about him. It was a strangely impersonal relationship that we had, considering how close we had been in all the years before I knew of her affair with my husband. Despite our superficial contact, something had been broken between us since we'd arrived in Lwow. Perhaps it was that Olek had asked me to take care of Maryla, and I had expected to have to protect her and support her. But in the event, she was the one who had the unearned income, albeit minuscule, and I was the one working from dawn till dusk in the soup kitchen. Perhaps I begrudged her. When I examined my feelings about that, I knew it wasn't the reason. After all, I was strong and glad to work, while Maryla was not. I was in fact relieved not to have to worry about her as well as Anna. Perhaps, instead, it was the fact that while she had had the affair with my husband, who had not contacted me in over a year, her husband was loyal and devoted to her, and did whatever he could for her and the children. She had taken something from me, and now she was depending on the man she had betrayed with Otto. It didn't feel like a loss at the time because I hadn't wanted Otto myself, but at this distance, their affair took on a different shape in my mind. Otto and Maryla had been happy together. They had obviously had strong feelings for one another, else how could the affair have lasted more than ten years? They had something which Otto and I had never had, something which I had only experienced twice, with Josef and later with Alexandre, and in both cases, I'd been forced to cut myself off from these people whom I had loved. Otto had, did, presumably love Maryla, and she had made no move to cut him off from her, to my knowledge. What is more, she seemed to have suffered no consequences of continuing their affair, as far as her relationship with Olek was concerned. She had her cake and ate it. What is more, she seemed oblivious of the hurt she had caused. She seemed able to maintain her gentleness and exhibited none of the traits of Jezebel or whoever that the story implied. She never ceased to be a nice person, and so I never found it in my heart to be angry with her. All that happened during the time we were together in Lwow was that my depth of feeling towards her left me, and by extension, my feelings towards her children. This felt somehow unsatisfactory, and I probably should have had an open and frank discussion with her about the way things were. After all, we could all go to our graves without resolution, and that would be a waste. But instead we had managed to maintain a superficially friendly relationship which revolved around caring for the children and worrying about making ends meet.

When Maryla came to my room on the day after she had received her travel visas from Conrad Brzozowski, she was flushed with excitement and evidently hugely relieved to be moving on.

"Oh Miriam, I'm so sorry that you and dear Anna will not be able to travel with us. I know that if Olek could have extended his diplomatic privileges to include you, he would have done. I'm sure that Otto has been working to obtain papers for you too, wherever he is."

"My dear, it is a relief to me that you and the children will be leaving this hell. I am sure that Olek has also made some sort of arrangements for you to travel on from Hungary, maybe to Palestine or North Africa, if what Isidor said is true. Perhaps you will find out what has become of Otto when you reach Budapest. For me, I will be hoping that I can at least keep out of harm's way until this war is over, and that Anna's health improves. For now, we are coping."

Maryla had brought with her a few items from her rooms, including her small stove, which she knew I needed, and an extra blanket. They were leaving on the train in the morning and could manage without these valuables until then. She also gave me what little cash she had left.

"It's so strange to know that I won't be needing Zlotys any more. Conrad gave me these. They're called Pengo – look, isn't it a strange currency?" She showed me a pile of notes, and some Filler coins, but I had no recollection of them from the last time I'd been to Hungary in 1917, on a hiking holiday with Paul.

"Miriam. I'm sure we will meet again before Christmas. If it is at all possible, Olek and I will send for you from wherever we can find safety. Aneta is so upset that she will be leaving Anna and Wiktor behind, and we will pray for you all. I feel terrible that we are leaving you. Please, forgive me."

"There's nothing to forgive, Maryla. This is the fate of this crazy world we live in. I'm just so happy to see people leave, although we will miss you all. It is not something you should feel guilty about. Just give my love to Olek and if he knows how to reach Otto, even if Otto can't contact me, please have him pass on my letters."

After she had gone, I sat staring into the empty grate and pondering our fates. I felt strangely cut off from my emotions. I was neither angry nor sad at her fortune and had long ago stopped feeling jealous of her.

CHAPTER 17

Factions

For months, people we knew of kept disappearing from Lwow. It was rarely talked about, and because we had nothing that could be called a social life, we all assumed that they had emigrated or managed to escape. Paul and Ada were friends with several people in the university, and through the engineering department, with lecturers and academics in other colleges. I had met a few of these people on occasion, but whenever I met Ada, she would tell me that one or another of them had gone. Anka's brother-in-law had been in the police, having joined as a young man in the early thirties, after the family arrived from the Ukraine. Since he'd lost his job to the NKVD, he had continued to keep in touch with what was happening in the prison through friends who'd kept their jobs, and he told her that large numbers of university staff were rotting in jail, charged with 'crimes against the revolution' by the NKVD. They regularly held trials in the prison, which were in camera and, he said, always resulted in mass deportations to Siberia or to summary executions in the prison yard. Meanwhile, Lwow University was taken over by Soviet academics. The Ukrainians, who had previously been unable to attend, were invited to study, and there were new Russian language and history departments apparently.

I also heard that a lot of residents of Lwow had been given Soviet citizenship, but that they had to swear some kind of allegiance to the communist regime. Those who refused were deported not to Siberia, but into the German occupied area of Poland. The NKVD were also systematically stripping local land-owners of their property, and daylight robbery was common, in which a team of NKVD would come for breakfast to one's house and leave it completely empty, like a swarm of locusts in a field of crops. They didn't just take the food and any alcohol, but also the furniture and the family's valuables. Sometimes they would kidnap an attractive teenage daughter, or a young wife, who ended up in informal brothels close to the police stations. These Bolsheviks were uncouth and unchecked, but they were also going hungry. They were men who had mostly been born in post-revolutionary Russia and had not known a time when the wealthy controlled the proletariat. They had grown up understanding that everything belonged to the people and should be shared out. They knew that owning riches was a crime against Russia, but they also knew that valuables could be exchanged for food and alcohol, both of which could be consumed without evidence.

It was a country, which supposedly cared more about breaking down class barriers than subjugating ethnic minorities, and for that, we had to thank our luck. Jews were not mistreated because they were Jewish, but only because they were wealthy. Unfortunately, there was a lot of mischief-making by the NKVD in encouraging gangs of Polish youths who roamed the streets to attack anyone whom they deemed part of the Polish elite, such as the academics and intellectuals, the Polish politicians, or members of the Jewish wealthy. NKVD patrols were given lists which they were encouraged to pass on to their contacts in the gangs. These ruffians lived on the streets by stripping others of their possessions, and it suited the NKVD to have someone else do their dirty-work, while instilling fear into the populous.

In a new twist, Ukrainians became the new elite, and we Polish Jews became an underclass. Anka was offered pay for doing the same job for which I only received my bowl of gruel, and while she continued to keep Inspector Mikhailov at arm's length, he insisted that she accept this pay. Indeed, had she not done so, he might have had her arrested as an anti-Soviet conspirator, working for the OUN, which was a Ukrainian independence movement. At least she was able to share a little currency with me to help pay the rent. We could no longer use our Zlotys, and what money she received was paid in Roubles. There was no bank or moneylender who would change the Polish currency into Roubles, and I was forced to sell my beautiful necklace to pay my way, one pearl at a time.

One night in April, the NKVD brought lorries into the centre of Lwow and loaded them up with anyone who had been involved with the Polish army, and their families, and took them away. They also took away large numbers of ex-police, who had been in the force before the war and had already lost their jobs to NKVD, but who were nevertheless considered a danger to Soviet rule. Anka's brother was lucky enough to have prior warning from his friend in the prison and hid in the loft of his house when they came to find him.

A month later, the same process was repeated and this time they took away any wealthy Jews who were left in the city. Thousands of people were pulled from their beds in the middle-class Jewish suburb north of the Lwów-Brody-Tarnopol railway line where Isidor and Ania had been living. My dentist contact was among them, and all the former Jewish Councilors from City Hall. Had Ania and Isidor still been in Lwow, they would undoubtedly have been taken then, if not before. There was terror among the Jewish community about who would be next. Only those, like us, with no money or property were left untouched at this point.

A Jewish resistance movement formed, mainly among the younger people, and these activists, who had initially supported the Russians because of their supposed egalitarian and left-wing politics, had now become very defensive, since the Ukrainians in Lwow were being encouraged to anti-Semitism. Gang fights erupted every day in the streets, and all the boys carried home-made knives with them for self-protection. The leaders in the synagogue were targeted for having helped the Russians when they first occupied the city and based on the accusation that they had denounced Poles who were involved in their own underground groups in Lwow.

Rabbis were tortured in the local prisons, and then executed. We heard of Polish gangs coming into the Jewish quarter at night and setting fire to homes of innocent people. I saw young men daubing doors with the anti-Semitic graffiti, and I read in a local paper, which Paul had picked up in City Hall, a Ukrainian backed paper, that we Jews were supposed to be part of a 'Judeo-Communist movement', a bunch of 'Muscovite Imperialists', and somehow responsible for the treatment of Ukrainians by the NKVD. When I first read it, I was amused by the rhetoric, and it made me angry to think that some politically motivated journalist had come up with such rubbish to sell papers. What good could it do to split the community with such inventions? It was easy to dismiss this as hyperbole and propaganda, but it was having a real effect on our safety. The history we'd always had, as long as I could remember, of division between Polish Jews and Ukrainians, and between us and the Catholics, was becoming a source of danger. But many times, Paul told me to hang on to my home and my work, to knuckle down and suffer the subjugation of the NKVD.

"For God's sake, Miriam. Don't react. You're as safe here as you will be anywhere in the city. You're already bound to be on the NKVD's list, since you work in that kitchen, just like I am for having got my job through the Planning Department. They might be a bunch of thugs, but that's all they are. You can see them coming at least. Anything is better than being taken over by the Nazis. Remember that."

"What do you mean? Are we about to be attacked by Hitler again? Surely he has agreed to keep back as long as Stalin wants Lwow for Russia?" My fears of Nazism were stronger than any I had for the Bolsheviks. All the stories we heard from incoming refugees were far worse than what we had to face in the city.

"All I know is that Hitler isn't to be trusted when it comes to Germany making deals with other countries, and there's no love lost between him and Stalin. We're powerless to do anything, and one way or another, we're probably all on an NKVD list for anti-Soviet leanings or on an OUN list for being a Communist, or on a Gestapo list for being a Jew."

"Who holds the list of good, honest, hardworking human beings?"

I thought Anna and I ought to move out of the Jewish quarter. I considered changing our surname from Wiener to something more Catholic and living as a gentile. I'd never really felt strongly about my race, let alone my beliefs. All that mattered was survival for me and Anna. On my way to the soup kitchen, I looked in the mirror in the doorway of the old tailor's shop doorway, cracked and blistered though it was, and I couldn't see any evidence of my origins, though it is easy to mislead oneself when it suits.

CHAPTER 18

Winter 1940

L ife became increasingly stressful as the summer faded and the cold winds arrived again from the east. We had no fuel and only worn clothing, and Anna was as thin as a rake. Her cough had not disappeared, and now she had diarrhoea all the time. There was no schooling or even any friends to play with, and the soup kitchen didn't allow me to bring her in to work, because they considered children to be a distraction for the kitchen staff. Every day, she looked after little Wiktor, but both of them slept a lot because they had so little nutrition. They lacked the energy to behave like normal children and besides, it would not be safe for them to be out on the street where other children were, crawling across the piles of rubble, scavenging in the ruins of bombed out houses or getting caught up in the melee. Gangs of teenage boys and even younger children sprang up and, working together, would have no qualms about daylight robbery or even fighting with home-made knives. Getting to work and home was now an obstacle course of street stalls and families living in the gutter, their children emaciated and barefoot, their begging hands out as we pushed past them. Many recognised me or Anka from the soup kitchen and we were always treated kindly by those who knew us, but were nevertheless seen as inexhaustible suppliers of food, even when we were not at work. Both of us had to secrete food under our clothing now, rather than carrying pots of stew or soup in our hands, and it was always difficult to resist giving what we had to the waifs dying of cold and hunger around us.

We worked harder and harder to try and feed everyone in the queue each day, and the quality and quantity of food in the stews we made dropped all the time. If we had one goat a week to butcher, we would make it last all week, mixed with root vegetables, grown in the nearby park by volunteers, who were allowed to jump the queue for their daily bowl of food in exchange for bringing us their produce. Gangs of hard working 'farmers' weeded and guarded their plots, and escorted one another along the street with their vegetables, so as not to be robbed. We knew so many of the faces of those who queued, but scarcely a day went by without someone telling us the grisly details of the death of one of their friends or relatives. We'd even had one or two people collapse, never to get up, while waiting to be fed. Despite these miseries, we didn't lose heart with the work, and if anyone in the kitchen slackened off at all, there were a thousand others waiting for their job.

The hardest emotion to deal with was the nagging fear that we would be rounded up and sent off to Siberia, or that the Russians might trade us Jews to the Germans in exchange for food or weapons. Lwow was only about twenty miles from the new German occupied territory border, and there was no demarcation or no-man's land, so as far as we could gather. Quite a lot of black market trading took place between the two armies near Lublin. We completely lacked any concrete information on the way the war was going, since the only papers in Lwow were controlled by the NKVD and full of local news only, and nobody had access to a wireless set to pick up radio from anywhere outside Lwow. In the vacuum, our imaginations ran wild. We hadn't been bombed for several months, but the number of arrests we heard about was increasing dramatically, and the number of Jewish refugees pouring into Lwow continued to increase, bringing with them stories of atrocities perpetrated by the Nazis in the west against Jews and Gypsies, Catholic priests, and Polish soldiers. Some were so far-fetched it was impossible to believe them. Someone told me about labour camps near Krakow where Jews were being burned in giant incinerators, and their bodies dumped in mass graves. It all seemed like a nightmarish fantasy perpetrated by the NKVD to subjugate the Jews, who they knew feared the Germans more than themselves.

We heard that Hungary was working with Mussolini and that Hitler was increasing his hold on Poland. We heard that Russia had left Slovakia to German rule and was looking to take over Bulgaria and Turkey. Nobody had any hope of a quick end to the fighting by then, and Hitler seemed to be bent on taking over the world, with Stalin's blessing. I'd wanted so much to hear from Isidor and Ania, but as the winter came, and the news of Hungary was so bad, I lost hope of hearing of them ever again. Even to know that they were safely away from Europe would have been a great boost to my morale, let alone any direct help from them. I wondered whether Maryla and Olek had been re-united and had managed to reach safety in North Africa or elsewhere, and whether Olek had managed to communicate with Otto. In all those months, I never faced the possibility that one or more of them had died in an effort to make their escape.

Paul told me that Russia was trading oil for German weapons, and while the two powers seemed to have very different objectives, they were happy to divide Poland between them and maintain a border. Ukrainian and Belarusian émigrés were apparently pleased to be Russian, which we found hard to understand, since Stalin's massive army was like a plague of locusts, removing everything of any use from our country. What was left in Lwow now had a uniform grayness. The city was like a giant cracked shell, teeming with scavengers, or a termite's nest, full of dark tunnels and writhing with maggots. I often felt homesick for Krakow, which had become some sort of a fairytale land in my imagination, despite the fact that we heard that it had been all but destroyed during the invasion and now that it had become the capital of the German occupied zone. The Jewish quarter was apparently no longer full of Jews, most of whom had been deported to labour camps, and I had to assume that the Germans had taken our property, along with all the others. All we got were shocking stories, which had passed through dozens, maybe hundreds of people on their way to Lwow. Occasionally we would hear stories, which had come through the wealthy elite of Lwow, who were trying to buy favour from Russian officers by entertaining and bribing them. We heard about the rounding up of Jews throughout the German occupied Polish towns and cities.

Anka said, "Ignore all the rumours. They can't possibly be true. Why would they bother to get rid of all those hard-working Jewish people who can slave for them?" But Anka was born a Catholic, and she didn't carry the history of subjugation inside her.

CHAPTER 19

Paul

L ife became monotonous, but under Russian occupation, we were at least safe from the Nazis. We managed to survive that winter without heat or ventilation in our attic room. And as soon as temperatures rose, and spring was with us, we tried to make the most of being outdoors. and we often sat outside on the steps of the house. I brought home Anna's portion of food from the kitchen, and when I had a few Roubles or something to barter, some root vegetables from the market. Anna became weak and thin, and despite Anka's best efforts to cheer me up, I began to be very depressed. She was now dating the Russian officer, and however much I liked her, and would not close my mind to individuals from another race being fundamentally good, it could not be ignored that she was in the NKVD's pocket now. People feared her at work and some tried to ask favours of her. Not least Martyna Kowalewicz, who now took Anka to her meetings with Boris Mikhailov, in order to get the best deal on food from the priest and to avoid having the NKVD confiscate all our meat.

Anka didn't get put on washing up as often as the other staff, and she started smoking Russian cigarettes, which she seemed to have a plentiful supply of. She offered me a whole packet one day, knowing that as I didn't smoke, I could barter them for a good quantity of vegetables. But I couldn't bring myself to accept them, as it felt like enemy contraband. Undoubtedly, had I traded the cigarettes in the market, I would quickly have been labeled as some Russian soldier's tart, since this was the origin of most of the cigarettes in circulation.

My friendship with Anka meant that people in the street, or in the queue for food, who knew about her and Boris, assumed I was also involved with an NKVD man, though nobody asked, and I said nothing. Without Anka to rely on so much for her positivity and support, it was hard to keep going. But there was no choice. No escape.

Ada came to the kitchen one morning in April. I'd only seen her there once, and that was when she arrived with Paul to tell me they were moving house because there wasn't enough room for them anymore. The landlord had been arrested and taken away, and since then, families kept pushing their way in and taking up squatters' rights in the hallway and outside their door. They'd been offered a room in a house owned by the Chief Engineer, who had survived several 'cullings' in the City Hall, because he was the only remaining person who understood the city's infrastructure. He had taken Paul in because Paul was the most capable assistant he'd ever worked with and they shared an understanding of the work. Paul was now the foreman of his team of repairers, and his boss wanted to ensure that Paul was well treated.

This time, Ada came alone. I saw her waiting in the queue as it shuffled to the counter. She seemed agitated, and I knew that she wouldn't have come for food, since she and Paul were well catered for at home.

"Miriam, please can we talk?"

"I can't leave my station for breaks whenever I want, you know, but if you wait a while, I am due to switch to washing up and you can help me and talk then."

When I looked over to her, seated in the corner, Ada was white and shaking, and I could see she was desperate to speak with me. As soon as the manager had left the kitchen I beckoned her in to the washing up area and while I washed the hundred or more plates piled on the side by Anka, who was cleaning tables, Ada stood by me with a tea-towel.

"They've taken Paul! He was pulled out at work and taken by the NKVD to Zamarstynowska Street prison. I just heard from the boss. They took three of his workmates too, all Jews. That's where they take the Ukrainians, the political prisoners and troublemakers, and you know they've been deporting them in trainloads. Siberia!"

"Oh God, Ada, have you been to try and find out what they're doing with him?"

"I went to the gates, but the guards threatened me. They said if I wanted to come in, they'd lock me up too. What am I going to do?"

"When I finish my shift, I'll try to find out. Go home and I'll come to you when I get some news."

Ada had to leave then as the manager came back and began to berate us for chatting rather than working, though she knew I was no slacker. When I left with Anka at seven, as the doors were being locked till the morning, I explained that I had to find someone who could discover why Paul was being held and what chance there was of his being released. Anka suggested that she could ask Boris, but I could tell she was loath to do that. He would consider the request a huge issue, and something which might make him look weak among his colleagues, helping a refugee, and a Ukrainian to boot. Anka, who is always so resourceful and determined, took me to talk to Mykola's brother, Marek, who had been in the local police before the invasion, and had, to her knowledge, worked in the police station next to the prison. Marek knew, like a lot of people who knew Anka, that she was dating Mikhailov, and she hadn't been to see him since that had all begun, uncertain of his reaction. Clearly, this was going to be a tough thing for Anka to do, since Marek had been so devastated by the news of his brother and would be disgusted that she would date an NKVD officer. He'd been best man at their wedding, as well.

"Anka, before we go to see Mykola's brother. You say he was a policeman and that he took it very hard when Mykola was killed. Do you think he knows about Boris?"

"Of course he does. The whole of Lwow seems to know about me and Boris! Miriam, I am sorry if he doesn't like me going out with a soldier, and a Russian. I know he can be difficult, but he'll just have to deal with it. He understands what it is like to lose a brother, and I am sure he will do what he can to help you. He's a decent man, underneath. You'll see."

We found Marek sitting on his front step, cleaning his boots. He was a heavyset man in his fifties with a moustache and grey hair. He got to his feet on seeing Anka and gave her a bear hug.

"Hello Anka, what a lovely surprise. How are you coping? How is Wiktor?"

"Yes, he's fine. I'm fine too. You're looking well fed, considering you haven't done a day's work in months." She grinned at Marek, and I could see immediately his resemblance to Wiktor, and the photograph which Anka had of Mykola.

"I hear you're popular with the NKVD these days, Anka. Mikhailov, isn't it? Is that why you haven't been to see me in months? Did you think I wouldn't be able to handle it? My brother's wife, going with the fucking NKVD? You certainly pick them, don't you?"

It was hard to tell whether Marek was angry or not. He didn't seem to be, but he might be one of those hard men who always have a smile on their faces, even when they mean one harm.

"Look Marek, I don't ask for your forgiveness for looking after my interests and Wiktor's. It's nearly a year since poor Myky died, and Boris is a good man. I know he's wearing the wrong coloured uniform, and that his lot took your job, but I made my choice, and you know me well enough to know not to argue with me."

"Don't jump to conclusions Anka. I was about to say that I love you like my own flesh and blood, and that Mykola would want you to be happy.

And of course, we can't tar everyone with the same brush. I heard he's OK as far as they go. But you won't mind if I don't stand as his best man… So, what brings you here now?"

"This is Miriam who I told you about, who lives above me. She's looking for a bit of help, and I thought you might be able to do something for her."

"Anything I can do for a friend of my sister-in-law and the mother of my favourite nephew."

I explained what Ada had been able to tell me, and Marek listened without interruption.

"Marek, do you think that Miriam's brother can be held without being charged? What do you think they will do to him? Is there any way you could find out for us? His name is Paul Blumenthal, and he was working down by the railway lines in Zolkiewskie." Anka put her arm round my shoulder.

"Yes, well. It's all changed since my day. Then you couldn't hold anyone for more than a day without charge, but now it's anyone's guess what they can do. The NKVD bastards are a law unto themselves. They've got hundreds of prisoners stashed in there, and there's only one or two people I know still working there. I heard they've been lining prisoners up and shooting them, to save having to feed them. I'm sorry, love, but that's what I hear."

"Do you think if you went down there, you could maybe find out about Paul?"

"Look, I'll ask a couple of the fellas I know, but I'm not making any promises. If they took him in this morning, he could be on a train out east by now. Hopefully not. If they have him in the cells, I'll see if I can find out whether he's OK. That's the best I can do."

"Thank you so much, Marek. Ada will be so grateful. Anka and I will be at the kitchen on Zadworzanska near the park, from early tomorrow, if you have any news."

Anka agreed to go back to the house with the food I had for Anna, and to look after the children. From Marek's place I walked to Ada and Paul's new lodgings, which took an hour, and told her what I'd managed to do. She was downhearted but grateful. I think she was already panicking that he had been executed, or deported, and I tried to placate her with the possibility that he was simply being held for questioning, though I knew, as she did, that the NKVD were prone to torture first and question later.

"Would you like to come back with me to sleep at our place? It isn't good for you to be on your own just now."

"But Paul might be released tonight and what would he do if I weren't here. He would worry. No, Miriam, I think I'd rather stay here. But thank you."

By the time I got home, it was already late, and I was exhausted, but worry over Paul's circumstances kept me awake. I spent most of the night thinking about him and how I should have spent more time with him since we'd lived so close to one another this last year, and how time had passed before the war and we'd rarely met for dinner in Krakow, despite my getting on so well with him and Ada. The image of him being tortured in that prison pervaded my thoughts, and it was the early hours before I finally fell asleep.

Paul had always been such a quiet person, even as a boy, serious and diligent. He'd studied hard and graduated from Krakow University with a first-class degree in civil engineering. He had been working for the Krakow City Council in the roads department after he graduated, designing a new main route through the city, and had met and fallen for Ada then. She was from Lwow, and they'd spent a lot of time here in the early thirties. Paul even said he would consider moving here, if she wanted, because he thought the grand design of the city, and its complex layout, would be a great challenge for his work.

Once I'd married, when Paul was eighteen and just finishing school, we saw much less of one another. He was preparing for university, and I was totally wrapped up in Otto's business life and travelling with him to see possible places to live in Danzig and Berlin, though I didn't want to leave Krakow. Paul and I had been so close as teenagers, with only eighteen months between us, and we'd often holidayed together, skiing and hill walking, before my ski accident. He had such energy for outdoor activities, and he was good company. I loved his dry sense of humour when it came to our evenings by a log fire in a mountain lodge or at some homestay in the country. We were quite different in our outlook, and it was impossible to raise any interest in him for politics, or business. He was a scientist really and had a passion for numbers and design. I think he would have been a great asset to Otto, running the sawmills, or designing machinery, if he'd been so inclined, but Paul didn't like Otto. I knew this from very early on, even when Otto came to court me, and Paul, who was only seventeen at the time, would be rude and disparaging about him. Later, two or three years after we were married, and Tomasz was still a baby, Paul had stayed over with us, and because Otto was out for the evening having dinner with some business associates, Paul tried to talk to me about my marriage.

"Miriam, I know it's not my business, but I want to ask you how it's all going with Otto."

"That's a strange question, Paul, and not one for a younger brother to ask his older sister. What do you mean 'how it's all going'?"

"I know I should keep my mouth shut. It's just that I worry about your happiness, Mimi, and I thought that you seemed a bit down today, and, well... "

"What?"

"Well, a bit short with Otto. He doesn't seem to be very, well, gracious with you, either."

"That's just his way. He's so busy dealing with the men on the docks and in the sawmills that he often forgets himself when he's talking to me, and he says things he doesn't mean. Or rather he says what he means, but he doesn't think to phrase it well. I'm perfectly used to his way."

"Really? You sound like you're excusing him. Are you OK together?"

"Mmm. I appreciate your concern, my dear, but a man and his wife have to deal with their own lives in a marriage, as you will find out one day. You can't interfere, you know. I'm not saying everything is perfect, and that I don't worry some of the time about how the future will be, but we have everything I could want. We have a beautiful home, a motorcar, and a housekeeper. Otto is ambitious, business-like, hard-working and well respected. We entertain, and I have time, and a generous allowance, to shop. Tomasz wants for nothing. He is a beautiful boy and he is so bright. Otto was the right choice for a husband, in many ways."

"That doesn't sound like someone who has fallen for their partner. I would only want to marry for love, and I will only do so when I have found my soul-mate."

"That's so easy for you to say, Paul. Men have that choice, especially when they are no longer under their parents' control, like you. For women, it's all about our parents' choice, and as you know, Papa and Uncle David made their choice for Otto. So, do you have a girlfriend?"

Paul blushed and became quiet. It was probably unfair of me to ask, since he was barely out of short pants, but I could see he was already an eligible young man, and someone with a passion about him. The sort of man I would like to have married, had I been given the choice.

I had almost no sleep before Anka knocked to call me for work. We heard nothing from Marek all morning, and it was mid-afternoon before he appeared in the doorway of the soup kitchen. He had a word with Martyna, whom he clearly knew, and she didn't try to intervene when he beckoned me and Anka over to a table in the corner. There was something about his demeanour that conveyed authority, as though he were still in the police force. Nobody dared cross anyone in authority, or even people who might have connections.

"Well, I've got some news. I was in to Zamarstynowska first thing, once I saw my old workmate, Alek Kowalczyk arrive. He was my sergeant, but he's nothing more than a warder now. Anyway, I caught him on the street before he went in and I gave him the name of your brother. He said he'd check for me and be back out to me. It wasn't more than a half-hour before he came to tell me that a Paul Blumenthal is in the cells with his three workmates and that so far they have not been questioned or mistreated. I asked him if there was anything he could do to help your brother, and he said to leave it with him, but he didn't sound that hopeful."

"Thank you so much for trying. It has to be good news that he's OK, and that he's not been taken away, doesn't it?"

"It's no bed of roses in there, I'm afraid. Alek told me that there's a lot of people dying of starvation and overcrowding in the cells, which have no ventilation, and then there are others that the NKVD does for. I'm not going to scare you with the details, but in the end, if he's on their list for the full treatment, you'd have to wish they'd taken him out to the yard straight off and..."

"For God's sake Marek, can't you see Miriam is upset enough without your tales. You did well, though. When do you think this Alek will let you know anything?"

"He lives down my road, so I'm sure he'll be on to me as soon as he has any news. I'll tell you when I have something to tell you." He got up, nodding to the manager to thank her for her patience.

"Anka. You could try your friend Mikhailov, you know. I appreciate that he's in charge, and it won't be easy, but you should see how the land lies with him. He only has to say the word, and they'll release Miriam's brother without harming a hair on his head."

I looked hard at Anka. It had to be her decision. We knew each other well enough for me to know that asking her outright to put herself and her relationship on the line for my brother was unnecessary. She would have thought through that already and would have made her decision.

"I know, Marek. I've been hoping Boris would have been in already this morning."

So, she had decided to ask him. I touched her hand and looked into her kind open face for a moment but said nothing. She looked worried, and I knew that she didn't expect Boris to help, and that the very fact of her asking him would jeopardise their relationship, since he could not appear to be doing favours for girlfriends in his position. Boris had always struck me as a hard and manipulative man who was only out for himself. He had that Russian harshness about him, and however strong Anka was, he was far stronger, and would, in my view, think nothing of crushing her along with all the others, if he chose to.

All day we worked hard, and there was no sign of Boris. It wasn't every day that he came into the kitchen, and perhaps he was off arresting Jews or supervising the torture of some university professor.

I was going to take the long walk to Ada's place after work, to check in on her, but she came to the kitchen as we were locking up and walked home with me. She said she didn't want to spend another hour alone in their home without Paul and asked if she could sleep on the floor in our room.

The next day, Anka talked to Boris, when he came into the kitchen for his breakfast, which meant that everyone in the queue was held back while he and two of his officers strolled to the front and took their bowls of stew, and slices of the very limited supply of bread we had. Boris sat at his usual table in the corner, while the other two sat a few feet away at the next table. They knew that he liked to have a chat with Anka and that he wanted privacy, but clearly also an audience, or maybe a security escort.

Boris beckoned Anka over to him to keep him company. I watched from the serving counter, as she chatted and teased him, and he seemed in a good mood. Then I saw her lean forward and, looking nervous, she became much more tentative in her conversation. Boris ate in silence, shoveling the food from his plate as he listened, and didn't look up at her. She finished speaking and put a hand on his sleeve. He immediately withdrew his arm, pushed back his empty bowl and looked up into her face. He screwed his eyes and frowned, and he seemed to wince, as though in pain. I saw him look briefly at his two colleagues, who were seated at a respectful distance, and concentrating on their food, then he whispered something to her. She looked blankly at him and he stood up and walked out. The two NKVD men left unfinished plates of food and hurried after him.

It was more than an hour later, when the stew had run out and the early queue had died down, that I got to speak to her.

"So, I saw you talking to Boris earlier, Anka. Did you get a chance to ask him about Paul?"

"What do you think? Of course I did."

"And did he offer to help?" I knew the answer before I asked the question. Anka had been silent and downbeat since he had left so abruptly, and it had obviously not ended well.

"Miriam, I'm sorry. I tried, but he won't help. We have to hope that Marek will have better luck."

"But what did Boris say?"

"You don't want to know. It doesn't matter."

"But Anka, you seem upset, and I didn't want to cause trouble for you with Boris. I know how much you like him. What did he say?" Anka was so open and frank, and we'd shared so much over the last year, I knew she wanted to unburden herself to me. It was more that she didn't want me to carry responsibility for her suffering that kept her from telling me the full story.

"If you must know, he told me that if I wanted to join some 'Fucking Yid trouble-maker' in the cells, he'd be happy to take me in. He accused me of . . . having relations with Paul . . . and he said that he wants nothing more to do with me."

"Oh no! That's terrible. He can't mean that, surely? I'm so sorry this has happened. Are you OK? Do you think he will come around and forget you asked? Oh God, I hope he won't cause more trouble for you."

"Miriam. I knew the risks, and I chose to ask. Excuse me for saying it, but Boris can go fuck himself. It was worth the risk, for your brother's sake, and perhaps now me and Boris are no longer 'an item', people will leave me alone."

For two days we heard nothing. Then Marek came to Anka's rooms late on the third night, and Ada and I rushed down from my room to meet him. Ada had been curled up on the bed for most of the last two days, and there had been a very strained atmosphere. I completely sympathised with her worry, and God knows I was worried too, but one has to keep going and she could have kept herself busy by helping out with Wiktor, since Anna is not well, but she did nothing.

Marek was different in his greeting, less off-hand than last time we'd met. I introduced Ada to him and he shook her hand and asked her to sit on the bed, while he stood facing her with his hands at his sides. She stared up at him in terror.

"OK, I've got to say that Kowalczyk did everything he could. Much more than I expected he would do. He took a huge risk. When they had your husband in the interrogation room, and they were taking a break in his interview, Alek let himself in. He has keys because he's the warder, and he works down in the cellblock. Alek didn't tell me what they'd been doing to Paul, but your brother was still conscious, because Alex said he managed to get his attention. He couldn't really talk to Paul, but he left the door open and said he was going outside the street door, which was just up the corridor, for a smoke. He couldn't exactly lead him out, but he made it pretty bloody obvious, he told me.

Then he went out of the interview room, up the corridor and stood outside the side door – you know that low metal one set into the wall on Sheremety – and waited for Paul to come out. He figured he could run him around the corner and let him off in the alley.

He did everything he could to get it into Paul's head that if he wanted to walk out of the jail, he could. He said he waited almost an hour, while the NKVD men were upstairs having their lunch or whatever, and in all that time, Paul just sat there and didn't dare leave. In the end, Alek heard them coming back down to the cells, so he had to go back in quick and lock Paul back in. It was all he could do."

"Oh God, no."

Ada burst into tears with her head in her hands. I sat down on the bed and held her to me. I was dumbfounded by Paul's failure to escape. How could he not realize what a chance was being offered to him, and if he did, why didn't he take what was offered?

"Do you know why your brother would've ignored the chance to get out, Miriam?" Anka asked.

"No, how can I understand? Perhaps he was confused, if they'd been interrogating him. Perhaps he was petrified that this was a trap. Why would he trust your friend? I know he wouldn't be easy to convince that risks are to be taken. He probably thought as he had nothing to hide that he'd somehow be allowed out through the front door, or else he just assumed it was a trap. Marek, did your friend say whether he's still OK? They didn't … hurt him did they?"

I couldn't bring myself to think about what that might involve, but as he hadn't been released, there was every chance they had worked on him in some way.

"Yeah, well, sorry to say he was put on the train yesterday to Siberia, along with about fifty others."

At that, Ada burst into a loud wailing, and shook from head to toe.

"Look, love," Marek sat on the other side and held Ada to him, "that doesn't mean the end, you know. I know it ain't going to be a walk in the park, but he's able bodied, isn't he? They'll put him to work, but they only shoot the people who can't work…"

"OK, Marek, that's enough. Let's not speculate. Ada and Miriam have enough to deal with without imagining Siberia."

Anka gave Ada a cup of water and laid her hand on my arm. I knew in my heart that Paul wouldn't come back.

CHAPTER 20

The Kitchen

May was baking hot. Anna was listless and pale, and hardly went out. The soup kitchen supplies became so limited we could only feed a small portion of those who came to the door, and by mid-day we were out of food, so Martyna closed earlier and earlier. Every day, there were scuffles in the queue, as starving street dwellers each tried to ensure they would be one of the diminishing number of people to receive a bowl of soup. There was no bread at all any longer. When trouble broke out in the queue, the NKVD started beating, and then arresting the starving refugees in the line who were fighting to survive. The priest who oversaw our work and was beholden to Boris to allow the continued kitchen service, told Martyna that she would have to close the doors if trouble continued. Boris and his colleagues had been to see him, apparently, looking for a larger share of the donations he was receiving, which were dwindling anyway. They threatened him with retribution against his church, and that they would have the soup kitchen closed immediately if he didn't comply but made it clear that it was the civil disobedience that would be cited as the reason for closing down the kitchen. He had to agree to provide the NKVD with more food from his parishioners, and he then came to Martyna and demanded that we bring our 'customers' into line if we wanted to keep our jobs. We tried to tell everyone to stop pushing, to wait their turn, and to leave peacefully once the day's rations ran out, but of course they were desperate and each saw that meal as their priority, and not their good behaviour.

One day, we had no deliveries of food, and we had nothing in the kitchen left over. I knew that the NKVD men had re-routed the food cart on its way from the church and taken our supplies for themselves. It had happened before, and we could do nothing to complain. In the past, we'd managed to improvise with what we kept in the kitchen from the day before, but that was when we had generous trades people donating to the church. Now that had all dried up, and the priest had been selling off the church silver and buying food where he could to keep the kitchen going.

We had to go out and tell everyone in the queue that there would be nothing for them. Anka, Martyna and I went together, as the largest and strongest staff, and we dreaded doing so. There was a lot of groaning and muttering, but most people turned and began to shuffle off. A group of about ten teenagers down at the corner, who had been waiting for hours already, began to shout at the NKVD officers who were standing across the street, keeping watch. They called them thieves and much more, and it was bound to incite them. These were the same three officers who were posted outside every morning, swinging batons and berating the starving refugees, or threatening them with beatings and arrest. The teenagers now shouting at them were part of a local gang who spent their evenings mugging people on their way home from work, and their nights breaking into local houses to steal what was saleable. They lived in a bombed out building near the station or under the old railway arches, and they were mostly boys, who would normally still be at school. The police were outnumbered, but were much stronger and armed with batons, while the gang of boys had only their homemade knives and the rocks they had found lying in the gutter. As they squared up to one another, and the three officers looked set to retreat, about twenty more NKVD arrived from the police station with rifles and began to shoot above the crowd.

Then they charged at the youths with their long batons raised and began beating everyone indiscriminately. Women and children were knocked to the ground, their faces bleeding and clothes ripped. Older men from the queue entered the fray, and some tried to grab NKVD men and haul them off. Anyone who fought back was beaten and kicked until they were inert. The Sergeant, one of Boris' regular entourage, who knew us all well and was generally civil to the staff, was shouting to everyone to go home, and threatening to arrest anyone who didn't do what they were told. The affray didn't last long, since it was so one-sided, and after half an hour, the street was deserted, and anyone who had been injured in the fight had either been arrested or carried off by their friends. The Sergeant took Martyna on one side and told her to close the place down, while his men came in behind the counter and confiscated all the pots and pans, taking them for the police station.

Anka and I stood helpless in the kitchen until everything was gone and the NKVD had left, then we hung up our aprons and walked home. Neither of us knew how we would continue to live without the free food we'd been depending on.

CHAPTER 21

June 1941

Ada was destitute now that Paul was gone and had no work herself. Ania and Isidor had been gone six months, and we had no idea whether they had made it across the border, or if they were languishing in some jail, or slaving in a labour camp, or had been buried in a mass grave after being executed. If anyone could pull strings, Isidor could, so we had to assume that they were OK. It would have been unbearable to think that both my siblings were beyond help. Paul, my beloved younger brother, might be working in Siberia, since it was summer, or perhaps he didn't make the journey. He might have escaped, or he might still be in prison somewhere. Not knowing was so intensely depressing, I couldn't bring myself to a point of optimism, and couldn't enjoy anything anymore. If he survived the torture they had undoubtedly subjected him to, and if he survived the journey, and then the back-breaking work they would make him do, he'd then have to survive a Siberian winter in a hut or hovel, and that would dwarf all other suffering. Other than Papa's death, I had had no experience of losing someone very close to me before. Unlike that time, when I was able to say my goodbyes to Papa, when he was on his deathbed, this was unbearable. There was no resolution, and not knowing what might have happened began to eat away at me. I felt so responsible for Ada even though I had no resources to offer her, and I felt helpless for the first time.

Anka joined Ada and me and we pooled our small amount of Roubles, which would last for a week or so, to buy bread and vegetables. Anka had found some work washing and mending clothes for a black-market trader who specialised in pillaging the homes of arrested people, or worse. Apparently he had a contact in the NKVD who would sell him the names and addresses of everyone who had been arrested each day, and those who had been executed, and he would systematically empty their houses of everything worth taking. She hated him for his work, and hated herself for supporting it, but he paid her in cash, as well as letting her choose items from his horde. She brought home clothes for Anna and shared her meagre pay with us. I considered selling my diamond, as I had so many times, but decided to hang on a little longer.

Tensions were mounting between the Jews and the Ukrainians since there was so little work and most people were starving. The Jews were seen by the OUN to be exploiting the Russian occupation and taking jobs, which had formerly been for Ukrainians. I found it hard to accept, considering that there were almost no Jewish employees in the civic offices, none in the police, and few working in the remaining shops either. Nevertheless, the NKVD were now employing Poles in the prisons and I heard from Anka that the Ukrainians who came to her boss for clothing talked about wanting the Germans to come and take over, to 'get rid of those Jewish Bolsheviks.'

Whatever was going on in political circles and whoever was joining one underground movement or another, it was clear that we couldn't keep going any longer.

"Ada, do you have anything left to sell? I have only one piece of jewellery left, and that's the diamond from my mother's engagement ring. I doubt anyone would pay what it's worth or even a fraction of what it's worth."

"I haven't anything now. Two weeks ago, I got just 25 Roubles for my last pair of earrings, from that thief of a money lender in the square. After I'd sold them, and I was careful not to be seen exchanging them for the money, I was followed all the way to my lodgings by some OUN men who must have been watching us from somewhere in the shadows. I wanted to keep some of the money, but I dared not, so I bought food and a pair of shoes."

"I'm worried that if the wind changes direction, the OUN will start hounding us. Sorry, Anka, but there seems to be more and more anti-Semitic behaviour among your people nowadays."

"My people? Who is my people? You are my people, and I don't care what religion you have or don't have, Miriam."

"OK, I know, and I'm sorry. I meant the Ukrainians who seem bent on getting rid of the Jews. But I do think you'll be under pressure to avoid us in public if this goes on much longer."

"Since when was I bothered by what people think? Didn't I put myself on the line with Boris for Paul? Besides, there's meant to be over 100,000 Jews here now, and that's a lot more than the Ukrainians. You have us outnumbered," she laughed.

Two days later, news came through on Lwow Radio, and spread out across the city like wildfire, that the German army had attacked Russians on their border, effectively breaking the agreement by which they had partitioned Poland. Russia had been attacking its neighbours in Lithuania, Estonia and Latvia, and had been moving into Rumania, trying to take more land. Since we knew that France had fallen to Germany, and that Hitler had most of Europe under his control, it seemed that Russia was his next target. Initially, He seemed ready to let Stalin take over more of the Baltic states, so that Russia could keep supplying Germany with raw materials, but that clearly wasn't his plan. The radio news said that there was a massive refugee movement going on with people pouring out of Rumania towards Germany, and that the Russians were stripping the refugees of their possessions as they fled, and the Germans were caught with the destitute influx at a time when they had shortages themselves. Since the fighting had begun the Bolsheviks didn't want to leave anything worth having for the German invaders and were burning and looting whatever was left, in their retreat east. It was clear enough to everyone that Hitler was now much stronger than Stalin and that Poland would be taken over completely by the Fascists.

"Anka, what should we do when the Nazis reach Lwow? I think we will all be rounded up and executed."

"We should flee, but we'll be stopped at the gates. The NKVD is already on high alert."

"So, what can we do? If we wait till the Russians retreat and leave the city open to the east then we won't have time to escape and if they stay to defend Lwow, there will be no time at all and we will be sitting ducks."

"Miriam. Couldn't you use your last diamond to buy some fake papers? Something that makes you a Christian, and maybe some travel permits? I'm not so concerned for myself. If the Russians leave, I will leave with them. I can go back to my birthplace and try to live off the land, if they open the gates, that is. But for you and Ada and Anna, there's going to be precious little hope under Hitler's rule. Maybe you should try to get something forged."

"Yes, you're right. I should try now, I know. If I can only find someone to trust who wouldn't take everything I have and abscond with it. I don't even know what a good fake looks like, it's so long since I saw a travel permit."

Two days later, the NKVD started rounding people up, almost without discrimination, and force-marching them out of Lwow, on the road east. We could have been taken, and we even considered joining the snaking line, taking our chances as prisoners of Stalin, rather than face the Nazis.

Then news came that there had been almost continuous gunfire from the prison on Zamarstynowska all morning, inside the yard where executions always took place. It went on all day, and it became clear that they were massacring prisoners, rather than letting them go, since all the NKVD officers were starting to leave. The OUN attacked the prison in the afternoon and managed to get in. They were trying to stop the killings of their relatives who had been locked up there for weeks. For a time, they seemed to wrest control from the officers, who were in disarray, but then the Russians moved back in and we heard explosions inside the building. The Germans were closing in on the city and vast numbers of refugees were already leaving on foot, with the retreating Russian army. We did not know what we could do to save ourselves, and even though I asked anyone I could trust, who was still in the city, nobody offered to help me with buying false papers. If he'd still been alive, the Dentist could have helped, and Isidor would have known who else to turn to, but it was unlikely that anyone capable would still be in Lwow. They'd have done their best work forging travel permits for themselves and would have left by now.

CHAPTER 22

Leaving Lwow

Anka and Wiktor left on Friday, because Marek and his wife had secured the use of a horse and cart. Though the animal was clearly starving and had been eyed up for slaughter by Marek for weeks, they felt it would be better to use the poor beast's last energy to pull their belongings and Wiktor, while they joined the walkers. It was a terribly upsetting experience for Anna, who had become like a little mother to Wiktor, and Anka and I spent a long time sitting silently holding one another's hands, before she left. There was nothing to say, except to wish one another safe keeping. We knew that our paths would never cross again, and that even if we both survived, and returned to our past lives, we wouldn't look one another up. Our relationship had been born of our circumstances and we had had no other reason than that to be friends. We had no culture or religion or education in common, and we were not even of a similar age. We'd worked hard together, fought one another's battles, fended for each other and fed one another. We'd helped each other's child and we'd kept each other company, held up our heads together through a long, hard year and more. We were more similar than we should be: both fighters and survivors, both fierce and strong, and both compassionate and generous. Anka had helped me to find all that in myself and I loved her dearly for that.

Ada had gone back to her lodgings after our discussion, to talk to Paul's boss, who was going to travel east with the Russians. He'd been able to continue with his work in the planning department because the Mayor trusted him, and he and his wife had been promised a space on one of the trucks, which were leaving. Ada hoped to be taken along with them, as a 'relative' and she promised to talk to me again before they left, if possible.

It was now Saturday, and I'd spent the day walking the streets, trying to find out if anyone I knew would help Anna and me. I had no more money, and only my diamond to sell. I had no work and everywhere there was violence being perpetrated against Jews by Ukrainians and the NKVD. I had witnessed beatings in the streets, and even saw two men kneeling naked in the gutter while an NKVD officer drew his pistol and shot them both in the head, before walking on, as though nothing had happened.

The streets were packed now with families carrying their meager possessions, as they headed towards the eastern gate, in a long line. It reminded me of the endless procession we had been part of just 21 months previously. It seemed almost surreal that we had been in the comfort of three expensive cars, in our fine clothing, still wearing our jewelry and with a hamper of rich food in the boot, waiting to be picked over. I couldn't remember the taste of meat, or the pleasure of even a glass of clean water, let alone the chance to sit in the soft leather of a driver's seat. Anna hadn't eaten all she was given then, and now, I couldn't find her enough food for one meal. And of all the adults and children in that convoy, only three of us were left here.

Ada arrived at the door as I was sitting on the front step, summoning up the courage to beg Mrs Wojcik for some food, if she had anything she could share with us. The landlady, Mrs Wisniewski, almost never came to the house any more. It was three months since she'd accepted with resignation our failure to pay her any more rent, and since there was nobody who had any money looking to rent property, there was no point turfing us into the street. We'd paid diligently for over a year, so she simply told us to look after the place, and she'd move back once the enemy moved out. It was a rare gesture of generosity, which I hadn't expected from her. She said that her sister was still receiving food parcels from her husband in the army, and it made sense for them to stay living together at her sister's house. Meanwhile, we already had eight families living in the Arkhypenka

Street house, which was bursting at the seams. Everyone was Jewish, and all had become extremely concerned about the Nazi invasion. It seemed to us inevitable that they would over-run Lwow in no time, since the Russians were showing no signs of defending the city. Most of the tenants were packing to leave in the morning, and I had decided that we too must go.

There was a distant thud, and then more, and we recognized the familiar sound across the city, as German planes flew overhead, having dropped their bombs on the defending forces at the western wall.

"Miriam, I'm leaving in the morning with Benedykt and Celestyn. They've managed to persuade the Mayor to put my name on the list of passengers in the convoy. We're driving out at 4 am, if the road is safe to leave by. I came to say goodbye and to ask if you have any plan to leave?"

"I've decided that we will start out tomorrow too, but we'll be on foot, and I am worried that Anna won't get far without help. I'm not strong enough to carry her, so I will try to find a space on a cart for her. I hear that the station is mobbed with people trying to board trains, but the NKVD are stopping anyone from getting near unless they have papers, since they are all heading for Moscow."

"I brought you a few Roubles from Benedykt, and a pot of vegetable stew which we have left. I'm sorry it isn't more."

"Ada, you have saved us again. I was waiting to see if anyone in the house had something to spare, but everyone is going without food today."

"I was thinking perhaps I could continue my journey to Siberia and try to find Paul there. I don't know where all the camps are, but perhaps there's some way of finding out, some sort of office in Moscow or whatever which keeps a record of prisoners."

"Ada, you must look after yourself, and trust God to take care of Paul."

I hated myself for making such a platitude out of the life of my brother, and her husband. He didn't deserve to be relegated to that. I knew, and had known since his arrest really, that Paul was doomed. Ada knew it too, in her heart, but unlike me, she was devout in her prayers and I'm sure she prayed for his safety morning, noon and night.

We hugged and she cried a little, and then she left. Anna and I finished the food she'd given us, and then Anna slipped downstairs to sleep in Wiktor's bed. She'd spent much of the last few months sharing with him, rather than cramped in our single bed with me, and now that he had gone, she felt so upset, it was all she could think to do to comfort herself. Anka's rooms were empty, but Anna knew every inch of them, and would not be scared.

I sat on alone, and wondered whether I would ever see Ada again, or whether she might disappear into my past like Paul and Isidor and Ania and Anka and Wiktor, and so many friends. I wondered if they were all part of a history and didn't exist in the present. Could they perhaps be characters and not flesh? What chance was there of ever meeting any one of them again? It made me think then of Otto, whom I had not seen for nearly three years. I couldn't really say I was still angry with him for our circumstances, or envious of his. I certainly didn't want him back, but he was still the father of our three children. I think I knew in my heart that Tomasz and Max were all right, and Anna still had a chance to survive, but everything would depend on my strength, and on the speed with which the convoy going east would take us to safety. I couldn't help a mirthless laugh at my own hopes. Safety? Why would it be safe? I didn't have any belief in the trustworthiness of the Russian authorities. They could stop the convoy in the middle of the forest and simply chuck out all the Poles, leaving us to fend for ourselves against the advancing Nazis, in an effort to reduce their numbers and make the food last longer. They could do much worse. It was already well known that they had been carrying out mass executions in the forests, and not even burying the bodies. The decision to join them was a huge risk for Ada, but I had noticed, since Paul's disappearance, she had a very fatalistic attitude. I wondered if perhaps she was better off with this attitude than I was with my dogged determination to survive. She no longer cared if she lived or died, unless she would see Paul again, and that made her choices easier.

I decided to wash Anna's clothes in the bucket, so that they would dry by the morning, and I would then sit down to stitch my few belongings into the sheet and add a makeshift strap to carry everything over my shoulder.

I was on my hands and knees, when there was a quiet tap at the door. I rarely had visitors, and then only by arrangement, so I was immediately scared that the NKVD had come for us. I would normally pretend not to be at home, and Anna was well used to hiding silently under the bed when people called during the day and I was at work, but somehow the quiet knock at the door reassured me it wasn't a threat.

I opened our door cautiously to find the doorway filled with the figure of a tall man. In the darkness, I couldn't immediately make out who it was, and I was terrified. I had no choice then but to open the door wider to allow some light to fall on the man's face. Momentarily I didn't recognize him, but then his familiarity began to dawn on me, and I was dumfounded. Standing on the landing was Alexandre Roskov, my dear friend from Berlin, whom I had not seen in five years.

I stood stock still, my eyes trying to take him in. My mind was blank at first, and then I began to realise that he was real, and not an apparition. He stood looking down into my face, unsmiling but in awe. I tried to take in what I saw. He was dressed in a grey overcoat, despite the temperature, and knee length black boots which were highly polished. He held a flat workman's cap at his side. Suddenly I felt fearful, without knowing why, and I glanced over his shoulder, to see that he was alone. I just couldn't believe that someone so precious to me was here, in Lwow, standing quietly watching my reactions, and that he wasn't an enemy come to take me away.

I was shocked by the change in his looks: his graying hair and lined, pale face, so different from the polished high colour he always had, and the loss of his handlebar moustache which he'd worn as an officer in the Austro-Hungarian army.

I was about to step forward to him when his coat fell open, and I saw under it that he was dressed in the uniform of a German SS officer. Alexandre was a Nazi! Of course, he was an Austrian officer, and would have been conscripted. My first thought was, 'Why have they sent a friend to arrest me?' But I had only to look into his eyes, and I knew straight away that he had not come in an official capacity. He could never hurt me. I knew it in my heart. However cautious one becomes when considering the enemy, one always knows instinctively to trust one's closest friends. I would place my life and Anna's in his hands in any circumstances, and now in this situation, I was certain it was all right.

He had taken a huge risk in coming into Lwow before the German army had taken the city, even though they were effectively in control of the region, and an even bigger risk in coming into the Jewish Quarter to find me. I couldn't understand how he had managed to locate me, though it transpired that he knew Conrad Brzozowski, and had been in touch with Olek as well, trying to find out where I was.

I was so taken aback at seeing him there, in his uniform, that it took me some time before I recalled myself and opened the door to usher him in. I quickly glanced up and down the landing behind him to see whether he had been observed. Luckily it was deserted. He had taken great care to cover his uniform in the coat, which looked just like an NKVD coat, and he wasn't carrying the peaked cap of a German officer.

He bowed, taking my wet hand, regardless of the carbolic smell from my servant's clothing.

"Miriam, I hope you will forgive my informal visit."

When he spoke, my heart felt fit to burst, and I was struck by how real this was. I must have been in a dream when I saw him first, and now that I heard his familiar voice, I felt suddenly terribly weak, and my knees began to shake. It was like a wave washing over me, mixing so many emotions. I felt hope rushing into me, and my heart seemed to flood. I felt so ashamed. How must I look? What could have brought him to me? Was he here to save me? Did he need help? After what seemed like minutes rather than seconds, I found my voice, and remembered my manners.

"Alexandre! How wonderful to see you. Come in, come in. I must apologise for my circumstances, and I am sorry that I can't offer you anything much except tea." I looked about me and realised how different our surroundings were to those of our previous meeting, in his restaurant.

When I looked back at him, Alexandre was staring in disbelief at the bare room, with mould on the walls and holes in the floorboards, and he only caught himself then to look into my eyes. I began to cry, as I remembered the last time we'd met in the Café Austerlitz in Vienna, and how we'd dined off fine china and drunk the best champagne, and how he had touched my hand under the table.

I had met Alexandre a good ten years before that, in the mid-twenties, just a few years after I married Otto. How splendid I must have looked then, in my beautiful blue silk dress and my diamonds, or was it that wondrous cream taffeta with the pearls? And, oh, didn't he have a monocle? Maybe not, I forget. I think I was on a shopping trip to Vienna. It must have been in the autumn of 1926, with the boys, since I remember that Max was still a baby, and I'd brought the wet nurse with me for him. Otto was away on business, and I was collecting some dresses I'd had made. Tomasz was six, and already doing so well at school. We always stayed with our friends, the Epsteins, who had a large apartment there. It seems ridiculous now, looking around my room, to think of the expense and luxury we took for granted then. I spent more on a hot chocolate in the Café Central then that I have spent on food for both of us in a week in the last six months.

That weekend, I had taken them to the opera, as a thank you, and we'd decided to go out to supper afterwards at the Austerlitz. It was their favourite restaurant, Stashek said, and they knew all the staff. It was so magnificent, with chandeliers and heavy white linen tablecloths and silver cutlery and cut crystal glasses. The waiters were dressed all in black with white aprons to their ankles, and a string quartet played Chopin and Strauss from the balcony overlooking the diners. That was a fairy-tale image even then, and now it was a fantasy I could hardly believe existed at all.

As we were leaving, Stashek introduced me to a tall, handsome man with a handlebar moustache and very stiff deportment. I'd noticed him earlier from across the room, staring unashamedly at me, and I'd been intrigued. He wore a tailcoat, waistcoat, wing collar, bow tie pinstriped trousers, and spats. He might have been the bridegroom at a wedding.

"Miriam, this is Count Alexandre Roskov. He is not only the owner of this fine restaurant, but also my good friend from the regiment. We were on the Eastern Front together, and I never met a finer soldier. Alexandre, may I introduce my dear friend Miriam? Miriam is visiting from Krakow for a little shopping, and we have just been to La Boheme."

"At your service, Madame," Alexandre actually clicked his heels. "I hope that you enjoyed our cuisine." He bowed stiffly from the waist to kiss my hand, something that was already somewhat archaic, but very charming.

"Are you staying long in our fine city?"

"Count Roskov. I'm honoured to meet you. Stashek has often talked of his comrades in arms. I must congratulate your chef on exceptional food, and your sommelier on his recommendations. No, I'm only here for the weekend, but I am often in town for shopping and entertainment."

As Alexandre straightened up, I was completely mesmerized by his blue eyes and the smile on his lips. It seemed that he wanted to tell me that I should come to Vienna to see him, and I knew that is what I would do.

"I can't believe how long it has been since we met, and how everything has changed."

Alexandre could not help looking down at his uniform with shame. He reached out to brush my tears away. It was the first time he had touched me since that evening, and his hand was shaking.

"I am so sorry that we have to meet in such different circumstances. I would so much like to turn back the clock to happier times. Vienna is no longer the city I knew, and so little is left of the Europe we loved. The world has been turned upside down by Hitler, and I find myself pressed into his service. You know it was not my choice, Miriam. I abhor the violence, and the greed and the racial myopia. I knew that if you'd managed to survive this long, under Russian occupation, you should not have to face the Nazi onslaught.

I had to find you and to try and help you. When I heard you were in Lwow, from a friend of Olek's, I knew it was imperative that I come and find you."

"But Alexandre, this must be so dangerous for you. I know that the Russians are retreating, and that Hitler will take Lwow, but haven't you crossed your enemy's lines to come into the city? What were you thinking?"

"I have been thinking of you for so long, and I have felt so powerless to do anything useful for you. I had to come, regardless of any risk. I'm afraid I can only stay a few minutes, but I had to reach you before it is too late. By tomorrow, I might not be able to help. You must know by now that the German army will be in Lwow within the next twenty-four hours, and once our army... their army... enters the city, you will no longer be safe. I have seen this in so many towns already. No, it's not that simple. I'm ashamed to say I have been involved in the process in so many towns, where my unit has entered, as the Russian soldiers have left, and we have rounded up all the Jews, and they have been loaded onto trains and sent to labour camps. This is carefully orchestrated, and there are lists compiled in advance of all those who must be arrested. The administrators, the Gestapo, have sources of information on all documented Jews in Lwow, based on the papers they have used in their work, and what they have taken from the NKVD through their spying. In my own work, I have access to a certain amount of this information, but it isn't my area. I do know about the plans to take the city, and to rid it of all its Jews. There will be nowhere to hide.

I came to tell you that my regiment will be first into the city, and we are tasked with the arrests. The lists are very comprehensive, and I am certain that your name will be in them, since Olek's friend informed me that you have been working in an official food distribution centre, and so you must have presented your papers."

"Yes, Alexandre, it is true, but surely, you have risked your job . . . no, your life…" I couldn't begin to understand what he had risked in coming to find me.

"I did what I had to do to reach you before it is too late. You must leave immediately, or you and your daughter will be taken away." He sat stiffly at the small table and accepted a glass of black tea. I stood at his side, and rested my hand on his shoulder, then stroked his hair, as the tears ran down my cheeks.

"You have been so kind to me always, and I'm overwhelmed that you have taken such a chance to come and warn me, but I cannot see what I can do to leave before tomorrow. We are unable to travel without papers, and I can't even walk out of the city without a permit. Besides, where would I go?"

"Without the right papers, you cannot travel, but if you have a Catholic identity, you can easily move out of the ghetto and you can travel, perhaps to Krakow where you have people you know well. You know I will always help you if I can. I have made enquiries, and I have still got some good friends here. I have arranged to buy some new identity papers for you both, and some travel permits. They will be drawn up tonight by a reliable man I have found, who deals in these things, and I can return later with them, provided I have all the information I need now. You must choose a suitable surname, and you must give me your ages, and an address I can use. How old is young Anna?"

"She's thirteen. But Alexandre, isn't this very dangerous for you, helping us? Will you not be found out? Also, I'm so sorry but I cannot afford to pay for these papers."

"Miriam, I have to live with myself in this uniform. Do you think I could live with myself if I didn't try to get you to safety?"

I had become so terrified of being picked up by the NKVD since the closure of the soup kitchen, and because of what had happened to Paul, I would have done anything for some forged papers for myself, and Anna, that did not show us as Jews. Many people in the quarter had traded their possessions, or their bodies, for such papers, and most had been let down by poor fakes or by false promises. I had almost given in to the temptation to accept an offer through my dentist contact to trade the diamond he knew about for papers, but had resisted, on the grounds that I didn't trust him enough. Now, my salvation had arrived in the form of a man I could trust absolutely, and someone who would do everything in his power to ensure our safety.

"Mrs Wojcik was my neighbour, and she's moved in with her sister. She's a Catholic and it is an easy name to remember. Wojcik. Miriam Wojcik, aged 41, from Krakow. Do you think it is enough? Can you really have papers made that will fool the guards at the station or soldiers on the roadblocks? I can't believe it might be possible. I don't know how I can ever…" I couldn't hold back my tears any longer, and there was nothing I could say that would express my gratitude. I handed him our documents in my married name, Weiner, and he took these as they had our photographs, and so that the forger could alter our names and address. Szeroka street is in the Jewish quarter in Krakow, so I gave Celestyna's address, which is in a Catholic neighbourhood, and at least if the Gestapo called there, and she was at home, she would have the sense not to give us away. I could visit her if we had papers and let her know. I had no idea how this would all be effected, but after what Alexandre had told me, these papers as they stood would be arrest warrants, and so would be no use to us again.

Alexandre left me his handkerchief and stepped quietly out of the room, saying he'd return as soon as he could.

True to his word, he returned two hours later, once it was dark, with papers in the name of Wojcik, for myself and Anna, together with travel permits and train tickets to Krakow. I had no idea how he had managed this since the station was in the hands of the NKVD, but Alexandre was always well connected in Lwow, and I could only assume he knew a local Pole who did a lot of the work for him in booking our tickets, once the papers were forged. I had never looked overtly Jewish, and my new identity as a Catholic Pole, gave me some protection. The papers were, as far as I could tell, as genuine as the originals, and had probably cost a great deal.

By the time Alexandre arrived, it was very late. I stood shivering on the landing, and whispered my thanks into his collar, as he held me. We both knew in our hearts that this might be our last private moment, ever. How could we hope to meet again in Vienna or Berlin or Krakow in peacetime? How could he and I both survive this war in our respective places, on opposite sides of the chasm, which Hitler's ambitions had created? Alexandre looked all of his 45 years and more, and he must be so tired. His poise was gone, his happiness too. Could he outlive this tragedy, and could we maybe see one another again? When Otto seemed to have deserted his family and failed us, only this man had come to our rescue, at any cost. I knew then, as I had known before, one true feeling for him, and I told him what I had never dared before, that I loved him.

Then, like a ghost, he'd gone, and I went down to Anka's room and crept into the bed beside Anna, to plan for the next day.

Early in the morning, after I'd heard the dawn chorus and lain awake wondering how the birds continued to live in Lwow, we rose quickly and dressed in all our remaining clothes. I carried our few possessions and we left the house without anything to eat. Alexandre had given me some Zlotys and Reichsmarks, as well as 25 Roubles, which he had kindly acquired for me when he bought the train tickets. He said I could use either the Zlotys or Reichsmarks in Krakow but that nobody in Krakow would take Roubles. If all went well at the station, my Roubles would not be much use to us by the end of the day, and if the Russian retreat continued as it had, the whole of Poland would become German occupied territory in a matter of days, and Reichsmarks would become the legal tender. For 25 Roubles, I could buy more food than we had seen in a long time, including bread and fruit, if there was any to be had. It was the first time in months I'd had any Zlotys and I had no idea what they would now buy in Krakow.

The room, which had been our home for eighteen months, was as bare as the day we arrived, and I had no hesitation in walking out without looking back. I felt very emotional about leaving behind the fear of being Jewish in Lwow, and the fear of starvation, but I was determined to make sure Alexandre's great kindness was not in vain.

"Anna. Before we go, I need to tell you that this is going to be difficult and scary. The Nazis are going to be asking us questions and checking our papers, and we must never, ever, say that we are Jewish again. Do you understand me? You are Anna Wojcik, and we are Catholics. You must not be scared, as I will protect you. Don't answer questions from soldiers. I will answer. Don't stop to watch anything you see which involves the SS officers. Keep your head down and keep close by my side. We will be home again in Krakow by tonight, if we are lucky."

Already a Ukrainian family who had been sharing Mrs Wojcik's rooms with several other refugees was carrying their meagre belongings up the stairs to our room, as we came down. The front door no longer had a lock, and was banging in the wind, though the day was hot. It was a Sunday, and I thought momentarily of going to the Catholic church to pray, or at least to be seen greeting the priest. As soon as we got to the corner, I realized how stupid I was being. The streets were awash with people, all bent on walking out of Lwow, as the German soldiers marched in. The noise and smell were overpowering, and we had to dodge our way between handcarts and men with large sacks over their shoulders. Women carried small children, and many people were bare-foot. They would not get far, though I doubted that the Germans would be trying to stop them from leaving, unless these were Jews, destined for arrest.

We had only been walking for a few minutes towards the station when we passed a group of Jewish people kneeling in the street with their hands above their heads, surrounded by German soldiers in grey uniforms, pointing guns at them. Each had the Star of David stitched onto their sleeve or breast, and they were all terrified. We hurried past with our heads down, as an empty truck screeched to a halt beside them and the soldiers roughly handed them into the back, ignoring their infirmity, or the helplessness of the children.

I thought of Alexandre's warning that they had lists of all the Jews to round up. My name and address were obviously on one of their lists, since I had worked at the soup kitchen, and no doubt, shortly, soldiers would arrive in Arkhypenka Street to begin clearing the quarter, house by house. It was no more than half a mile away, and they were bound to be working quickly and methodically. They would probably be looking for Miriam Weiner within hours, if not already, but I was no longer her. I was Miriam Wojcik, and that small change could save my life.

We heard shots in one or two of the houses we passed, and we saw some people, who ran from their houses, being shot in the street. Their bodies were left in the gutter as soldiers ran past them into the houses. Screams and cries came from windows, and I even glimpsed someone climb out of a third-floor window and jump to their death below. This carnage was more shocking than anything I'd seen from the NKVD.

We walked for half an hour, and stopped twice to buy food from street vendors, neither of whom spent long haggling, since they seemed more intent on packing up their stalls. We approached the station with trepidation, and already the German soldiers surrounded the entrance, and had taken over the ticket office. We queued for a few minutes and as we came to the head of the line, I realised that this was the first test of the forged papers. The young Nazi who took my papers and the train tickets for the mid-morning Krakow train looked at the photo and into my face, and then handed me the papers and ushered us through the barrier. If he could have known how fast my heart beat, we would have been questioned, but everything passed muster and we were onto the platform.

CHAPTER 23

Krakow

The journey was interminable, as the train stopped three times for identity checks. Each time I cowered before the Gestapo officer who came with his escort of SS to check everyone's documents, and thankfully everyone else in the compartment seemed as scared as I was. But with Alexandre's papers and permits, we arrived in the late afternoon without difficulty into Główny. As the train rolled into Krakow, through the suburbs, I watched the familiar roofs and terraces, and hoped to feel relief, but it didn't come. My stomach was in such a knot and my heart was in my throat for fear of arrest that I couldn't begin to enjoy the feeling that we were home, miraculously escaping the hell of Lwow.

The station had changed. Not physically, but the place was teeming with soldiers, all in Nazi uniforms, and we saw few civilians who weren't either walking fast with their heads down or queuing at gates to have their papers checked. The station café was occupied by SS officers, and nobody else, and the whole place seemed like a barracks. I could see swastikas everywhere I turned.

There was no choice but to walk, but then it was so long since we'd used a taxi or driven in a car, I might have chosen to walk even if we'd been offered a lift to the house. It was late June and the sun beat down on us as we walked. It felt more oppressive than it should have done. After all, it was a beautiful summer's day and Krakow, my home town, was still the same place. But bricks and mortar don't make a city what it is. The boulevards were lined with army paraphernalia and tanks drove up Stradomska towards Wawel Castle, as though they planned to destroy it with their shells. It might have stood for eight hundred years, but then

I was sure it would take a few hours to reduce it to rubble, along with the Jewish quarter to which we were headed. I'd thought on the train of not going back, and simply looking for accommodation in another part of the city, but I couldn't help myself. I thought perhaps we could enter the apartment quietly and collect some of our belongings, at least.

Avoiding the main square, where there were squads of marching soldiers and large numbers of armoured vehicles, we walked the mile to Kazimierz through the familiar back streets, with our heads down and covered in scarves. Turning onto Szeroka street, with its familiar plaza and gardens, surrounded by bars and cafes, I had to stop and hold onto a railing as I began to feel faint with fear. The Jewish quarter I had known and loved since childhood was unrecognisable. It had been turned into a Nazi social centre, full of revelers and prostitutes, and the bars were spilling grey uniforms onto the pavements. When eventually we made it into Gazowa and could see the Vistula flowing swiftly in the evening light ahead of us, I pulled Anna quickly into a narrow passage opposite our apartment. We stood quietly, watching. There were German soldiers on the pavement outside, and a large army jeep parked in the driveway. The anti-Semitic graffiti, which I remembered from eighteen months ago, was still visible on the gate, though it had faded.

"Mamushu, why can't we go indoors? I'm tired of walking and I want to go to see my room again."

"Shhh. We can't go in, because it looks like there are soldiers living in the house. Let's just wait here and see whether we will be able to go in or not."

There were lights on in the lounge windows on the first floor, and it was clearly occupied. We didn't have to wait long. Within minutes, the door opened and three SS Officers came out, chatting and smoking, and strolled towards the bar on the corner.

"I'm sorry, darling. I know you're tired, but we can't go home now." I whispered to Anna, who had said nothing, though I could see her chin begin to shake and a tear ran down her cheek. "Remember we changed our name only yesterday to Wojcik. If we were to go into the house now, they would arrest us as Weiners and we would be taken to jail."

Anna was used to saying nothing and doing exactly as she was told. "We'll have to visit someone else's house tonight and see whether we can stay somewhere else for a while. I know, we'll try the Epsteins. You and Emilia played together last time we all met in Vichy, if you can remember. They live across the river."

We crept out of the alleyway and in the dark, crossed the river to Podgorze, a quiet leafy suburb where Stashek and Gabriela lived. Otto and Stashek had been school friends, though Stashek's parents were good Catholics, and we'd been invited to their wedding. Gabriela had always been one of my confidantes. She was very intelligent and understood much more than I told her about Otto and me. We used to dine with them regularly before the war, in that different world, where I spent so much time and money on dinner parties. When there were not endless lines of starving people waiting for a bowl of gruel, and when I had nothing more in my mind than how to occupy my time with social entertainment.

Their street was some distance from the river, and we were becoming more tired as we walked. Neither of us had eaten much, since there was little to buy in Lwow, and once we'd arrived in Krakow, all we wanted was to get home. Now it was growing dark, and we crept along in the shadows. There were few people on the street, and I realised that perhaps there was a curfew. But it wasn't late, and this smart suburb was probably being used by senior Nazi officers and their families. Indeed, we'd seen one or two large cars driven by SS officers turning into the gates of houses as we passed. Stashek had been, as far as I knew, conscripted in the first days of the war, and so would presumably be gone. He could, heaven help him, be dead, and Gabriela could have been thrown out of their home by now. I hoped desperately that she would be at home still. To my great relief, she opened the door as soon as I knocked. It took her a moment to recognise me, despite little more than two years having lapsed since we'd met.

"My God! Miriam… and Anna. I hardly recognized you. Come in. You look… exhausted."

Gabriela was shocked at seeing us. Of course, she had probably assumed that we had been taken off to a labour camp, having been in Nazi occupied Poland since the start of the war. She looked well and smartly dressed, and we looked like two tramps, emaciated and dirty. Our clothes, though fairly clean, were torn and worn, and Anna looked like a ghost of her former self, as well as being six or eight inches taller. I suddenly caught sight of my face in the hall mirror. It was the first time I'd seen myself reflected in weeks, or rather the first time I had looked. What I saw now was an old woman, who looked like a skivvy. My hair was completely grey, which it hadn't been when Gabriela last saw me. Though I had my colour done once a week in the thirties, it was only to cover one or two stray grey hairs. My face was deeply lined, and my eyebrows had grown bushy.

"Miriam, where have you been? How have you managed? And how did you get here without being arrested? Oh God, it's such a relief to see you both." She took me in her arms, and I began to cry. I shook and cried and couldn't stop. I knew it was relief that brought me to tears, but once the dam had burst, I couldn't hold back the waters, and Gabriela had to lead us to her lounge, where we collapsed into the soft sofa. She handed me a clean white handkerchief, and I stroked the fine fabric for a while, just for the pleasure of touching it. Anna was already curling up onto the sofa, like a cat looking for comfort.

"I'll make us some tea. I wish I could offer you something stronger. You look like you need it. I haven't a great deal of food, but I'll heat up the bigos. I know it's pork, but you're not Kosher, are you, and you both look like you need some good food."

"Thank you, Gabriela. You don't know how much it means to find you. It has been so long. Everything has been so . . . difficult . . ." I couldn't help myself but began to cry again. Gabriela left us while she went to the kitchen to make tea, and I was glad she did. Anna had fallen asleep immediately, and I was able then to sit in silence, in the safety and familiarity of a comfortable room, in a peaceful house on a quiet street, knowing that I wasn't in immediate danger, with my new identity. I felt sick, and immensely tired, but the relief was like a wave of warm water washing over me. I closed my eyes and must have dozed.

Gabriela woke me with a mug of hot tea, which had sugar in it. Something I hadn't tasted for over a year. Then she put two bowls of bigos on the table and I woke Anna to have something to eat. The food was rich and spicy, and I quickly began to feel nauseous because I was so unused to meat. Anna couldn't eat her food, as she was so tired, and she too felt sick.

"And where is Emilia, Gabriela? Is she already in bed? Anna would love to see her I'm sure."

"No, I'm afraid she isn't here. It hasn't really been safe here in Krakow for a long time, and I didn't want her to be on her own when they closed the schools. She's living with my sister Helena, in Czestochowa, and I visit when I can get a travel permit. Stashek has been in England for some months now, where he has joined up with the Polish Free Army. We rarely hear from one another, because there is only sporadic post, and it is impossible to phone abroad. He would like me to join him there, but I have found it impossible to travel, and so we live apart. But tell me, Miriam, have you heard from Otto?"

"Gabriela, I have so much to talk about with you. Let me first take Anna up to bed, if I may, and then we can talk more." I didn't want to discuss Otto in front of Anna, and besides, she was badly in need of sleep now.

"Sorry, Miriam, what a poor hostess I make. Please let me offer Anna Emilia's room. The bed is made up and there's hot water if she would like a bath."

"Hot Water! Do you hear that, Anna?"

But Anna was so tired I decided that we would leave bathing till the morning. I took her upstairs and put her to bed in Emilia's bed, and for the first time in so long, she was able to curl up under the covers with a soft toy. Despite her fourteen years, she looked like a small sick child, lying there with her white face against the pillow. She smiled at me when I bent to kiss her goodnight.

"I'm so glad we're back home again, Mamushu. If only we could have our own house back, and then everything would be alright."

"Sleep now, Anna darling, and in the morning, we'll see what we can do about finding somewhere of our own to live. We must put our best foot forward, and we need to find you a school. I need to ask auntie Gabriela who is here and whether there is anywhere I can get work. Now go to sleep. I'll be up myself soon."

For the next hour, I told Gabriela about our flight from Krakow, through Naleczow to Lwow, and about the family, all of whom she knew well. I told her everything except how I obtained the false papers. For her part, Gabriela told me about life in Krakow under German occupation, and how part of Podgorze had become a ghetto for thousands of Jews behind a newly built wall, and how the SS guarded it like a prison, regularly tearing people from their homes and taking them away for work parties in the city. There were apparently groups of Jews who were trying to resist, and regular skirmishes by the ZOB, a youth movement, which found ways in and out of the ghetto. Living on the gentile side of the wall was relatively bearable, and Gabriela was able to draw money from their bank account, though it was now in Reichsmarks and the exchange rate with the Zloty was ridiculous she said. I wondered if Otto's domestic account was still accessible. Each month he had deposited my allowance, and perhaps I could now obtain funds. But that would mean using my married name, for which I no longer had papers, and besides, Gabriela told me that the accounts owned by Jewish families had been cleaned out long ago.

"So, now we are alone, tell me when did you last hear from Otto?"

"I have heard nothing in almost two years. When war was declared, he demanded I return to Poland from Paris, when I intended taking Anna to London with Max and Tom. Meanwhile he wasn't intending on returning from Hungary and had some hair-brained scheme to enlist in his old regiment, which I assume he did. If I had only ignored his demands, I would have been safe and with all my children, and not trapped in hell. If I hadn't made it from Naleczow to Lwow with Ania and Paul and their families, and Maryla too with her children, we would all have been arrested as Jews. And once we were in Lwow, under Russian control, life was miserable."

"Stashek was in touch with Otto in Hungary last year, before he left Poland. Otto was trying to contact you and he couldn't find out where you were. We didn't know, and Otto was hoping that Olek might know someone in the diplomatic service who could find you."

"Yes, he does, or rather he did. Conrad Brzozowski was his name, and he was very helpful to Maryla when we first arrived in Lwow. He managed to give her money, which Olek had asked him to do, and eventually he also arranged some papers for her, Szymon and Aneta, to join Olek in Budapest. I gave them letters for Otto, and that was the last I heard from them. Unfortunately, Brzozowski was taken away by the NKVD soon after that, because of his political connections, and I doubt he is still alive. If Maryla joined Olek, she would have given him details of where we were living, and if Olek and Otto were in touch, which I assume they would have been, then Otto should have received my letters and must have known where we were."

"Perhaps, but I am sure it would not have been possible to contact you without some contacts who could travel freely between Budapest and Lwow. "

"Gabriela, I have for some time given up on Otto, and it is no use speculating about what he could or couldn't have done. I just need to manage on my own now, and with the help of some remarkable people whom I met in Lwow, it has been possible to survive all this time."

"And how did you manage to travel from Lwow. I hear that Hitler's declaration of war on Stalin has meant that the Russians are retreating and the Nazis are advancing on Lwow."

"And they have now taken the city. In fact, as I boarded the train yesterday, they were in the Jewish quarter, rounding people up and pushing them into lorries."

I decided I couldn't undermine what Alxeandre had done for me by denying his place in my rescue. I then told Gabriela the whole story about Alexandre coming to our rescue, though I didn't detail my past association with him, since I assumed that anything I said to her would at some stage be passed to Stashek, and then on to Otto. Though frankly, at this point, I do ask myself whether I care that he might know. It was, after all, Stashek who originally introduced me to Alexandre, as they had both been soldiers together in the Great War, and he and Gabriela knew him well enough. When I told Gabriela who had come to find me, she didn't express great surprise. Perhaps she knew all along what was between us. Alexandre had once told me that Stashek had asked him about me, and whether he was behaving 'honourably' towards me. At the time, I didn't think they knew, as we had only met a few times when I was in Vienna, and never with them after that first introduction, but Gabriela was very intuitive, and I could sense even now that she knew.

"So, Alexandre Roskov, who is now an SS Captain, is in Lwow with the vanguard of the invading forces, and his unit is responsible for supervising the arrest of Jews, and yet he helped you to escape his own men. That is a miracle. Why would he risk so much for a Jewess? But then again, in war, many strange things happen. I always knew him to be a fair-minded man and could not begin to understand how someone like that could cope with Fascism. And he made the arrangements for you to receive forged papers in the name of a Catholic, in one night, so that you could escape from the enemy in the last moments before they would have hauled you off to a labour camp. It truly is a miracle. And with your new name – Wojcik, you say – you are effectively as free to travel as I am. Amazing!"

"Yes, that's true. But with that name, I am now unable to access my past. I'm no longer Miriam Weiner, and any of my Jewish friends who are still here will almost certainly be living in that Ghetto you told me about, poor wretches. My money is not available to me, and I have nowhere to live, and no work. Gabriela, I'm at your mercy I'm afraid."

"OK, let's sleep on that and in the morning, when you've had time to enjoy some home comforts, and I've found some clothes for you and Anna, we can talk about the future. For now, I am deeply grateful to whatever angel has looked over you."

"Thank you. I'm afraid I lost what faith I had a long time ago, when I began to see what atrocities have been perpetrated against innocent people. There is no God that could let happen what I have seen."

CHAPTER 24

Moving On

The next day we spent talking about the future. Gabriela was concerned about my new identity being unmasked in Krakow, since I had so many friends and acquaintances who would recognise me, and quickly alert the Gestapo, either intentionally, or by association. It was not obvious to me initially that there would be informers among the Jewish population, though Gabriela told me that it was so, but apparently the Gestapo's level of influence, through so many pressures they brought to bear on people, was enormous. There were shop keepers whom I had known to say hello to, who held accounts in Otto and my names, who would recognise me, and would also be in the pay of the Gestapo, or under threat of arrest for non-co-operation. If I were to be seen on the street by someone who greeted me, the next thing might be a knock at Gabriela's door from the SS.

"Miriam, I know you want to work, and it is possible to work in an office now, since you have Catholic documentation. There are probably jobs to be had for good secretaries, but you cannot afford to be recognized. I speak as a Catholic who knows the mind of my neighbour. Whilst many are indifferent to the Jews' plight, there are more who feel that while the Nazis have been focused on rounding up the Jews, they have left the Catholics alone. When the troops arrived here, after you'd left, they persecuted our priests and so many were arrested, and even though Pope Pius has done a lot to help Jews escape from Hitler's attacks, he has kept his head down when it comes to denouncing the Nazis publicly. I think that if you are known to Catholics in Krakow, quite quickly, you will be known to the Gestapo, who are cracking down on people with false papers here."

"That is valuable to know. I will have to consider moving on, as I must become independent, and the last thing I want is to put you in any danger for harbouring Jews. I heard in Lwow that the labour camps are being used for mass killings, and that ghettos are being set up across Poland to help the Nazis corral all the Jews, so they can be sent to their deaths. That's the story coming from refugees who were arriving into Lwow in the last month or so. It's going to be unsafe everywhere, but from what you say, it will be more unsafe where I can be recognized."

"So, I have been thinking. Would you consider coming with me to visit Helena, to see Emilia. You remember Helena coming to dinner with me and Stashek at your invitation a couple of years ago. She is very able and well connected in Czestochowa and I can write to her to tell her that my friend Miriam Wojcik is coming with me because she would like to move for work. Helena can look for an apartment for you and Anna and may know of a job that would suit you, since she's been running an office that deals with recruitment across the city. She will know you are Jewish, but she will not tell anyone."

"Thank you, Gabriela. That would be ideal. But is it a slow process to access a travel permit to visit?"

"For me, I can easily get a one-day pass which is enough for my monthly visit to Emilia. You would probably be able to do the same, but just not return to Krakow. I doubt that the authorities in Czestochowa would be checking on whether you returned to Krakow, and you have not registered your presence here, so nobody at this end would be looking for you to be here. The Gestapo are incredibly thorough, so I presume the only issue will be whether your ticket from Lwow to here will be checked."

"Well, let's do as you say. Can you send a letter to Helena, and I will keep a low profile till we travel, so as not to be recognized? I would so dearly like to be able to get into the apartment and see if our belongings are still there. I would love to replace my clothing and Anna's. Also, I would like to contact Celestyna because she is looking after some of our valuables, and since I have none of my jewellery left, I would perhaps be able to raise some cash from the sale of one or two things."

"Miriam, if you are short, I can help you a little, and Helena will make sure that until you are employed, you won't starve."

Within two days, we were boarding a train to Czestochowa, with Gabriela, on a day pass. When we got to Helena's house, Anna and Emilia were like two sisters, and I was heartened to see Anna smile for the first time in months. Helena was as I remembered her: a tall, stern, middle-aged woman with a straight back and her hair tied up in a tight bun. She wore a dark suit and seemed very focused on her work.

"Good afternoon, Miriam. I'm so pleased you could come. I so much enjoyed meeting you before the war, and to hear about Otto's business. I had hoped to open an office in Krakow with Gabriela and Stashek's help, before everything changed. Now I am struggling to keep our business running here. Gabriela's letter told me that you were coming for work and would welcome my help with accommodation."

"Yes, I would be most grateful of any help you can give us." I pulled my forged papers from the handbag that Gabriela had lent me and passed them to Helena. "As you can see, I am a Catholic and if possible, I would like to move into the area around Jasna Gora, so that I can attend daily mass. I've been reading as much as possible in some of Gabriela's books to make sure I will fit in."

"I have a friend who rents rooms, and she will be able to find you something. But first you may be interested in a secretarial job I am trying to fill, in a firm of solicitors. They need shorthand and good typing speeds. I expect you may be a bit rusty, but I have a typewriter upstairs, and I have made you a bed in our spare room. It should help you to settle for a couple of days while you prepare for your interview, and I will invite my friend over to meet you here. I hope that is all acceptable to you. I felt it would be best to make advance plans."

"Helena, you have done so much for us, and we don't want to impose on you, but this is so very generous. You're right, I will need to practise my typing and shorthand before I can apply for secretarial work, not to mention Anna and me attending mass with someone who can guide us through the service."

"Good. That's settled then." And Helena went to make tea for Gabriela and me while the girls played in Emilia's room. From that moment, Helena never asked me a question about the past, and never referred to my Jewish origins even in private.

I said a fond farewell to Gabriela, when she left to catch the late train home, and I could see how upset she was to leave Emilia behind as she returned to Krakow.

CHAPTER 25

Relative Safety

The city had been occupied by both Russian and German armies during the Great War, but because it was a very important religious centre for the Catholics, it had been protected until the Germans occupied the region in 1939. I found that the Jewish Ghetto had already been subject to regular Pogroms, and over the next couple of years, about 45,000 Jews were taken from Czestochowa and killed, though I didn't know about that until much later.

I spent two days brushing up on my secretarial skills and getting ready for my interview, and Anna and I also met Helena's friend who was a landlady in the Catholic district. She told us she had rooms available, and that we should come to visit her before committing to them in case they weren't to our satisfaction. She obviously held Helena in great esteem and assumed that we were friends of Helena and should be treated equally well. It amused me to think that there could be rooms in this lovely town, in a Catholic neighbourhood, which would not meet with our approval, given our experiences in Lwow.

She lived in a large house on Karola Szymanowskiego, just a couple of streets from the park and the museum. I thought the area was quite grand, and her house was an elegant double fronted three-storey home divided into six apartments, which were all fitted with quite comfortable furniture. After Lwow, it was positively palatial, and I would have expected it to be well outside my earnings, but when I asked Mrs Lisowski, the rent was quite low. Later I found out that Helena, ever the business-woman, had negotiated a preferential rate for me, because she would do anything for Gabriela and because of my need of a better life. It struck me that before the war, we wouldn't have considered Gabriela and Stashek's religion as a point of difference. Besides the wedding mass, neither they nor we had been church-goers, and Stashek was positively atheistic, as we were. Helena also showed no sign of attending mass on the Sunday after we moved into her house, but I could see crucifixes in each room of the apartment in Mrs Lisowski's house, and it struck me that Helena may have chosen this place purposefully.

Mrs Lisowski was a friendly woman in her fifties, with a tired expression and too much face powder under her grey hair. She wore an apron and had clearly been mopping the floor when we arrived into the hallway.

"I have always had a home help, you know, but since the occupation, it has been hard to keep staff," she said, eyeing up Anna. "I could do with a young helper, if your daughter wanted a few hours work each week, after school. Anna, isn't it? Well, Anna, I expect you haven't enrolled in the local school yet, so perhaps you can give me a hand till you start?"

Anna had neither the energy nor the inclination to become a skivvy, and I wasn't going to allow the landlady to take advantage of her.

"Anna must study a lot, Mrs Lisowski, since she has missed a lot of school recently due to ill health. I'm not sure that she would be much use to you, even if she had the time to help. She has to rest every day between her studies. What time is morning mass at Jasna Gora, please?" I asked in as off-hand a way as I could.

"I don't know anyone who attends mass there, Mrs Wojcik. It is a convent, you know, and it's really only high days and Christmas when the locals visit it. It takes a while to get there, you know. We usually attend Niedziela, which is a lovely small church, and the priest is very devout, you know, and after all, it is much nearer. They have mass at 7am, if you want to go before work. Otherwise it's 10am. You should of course visit Jasna Gora to see the Black Madonna, which is so famous, but if you have visited before from Krakow, I'm sure you have been to pray to her, haven't you?"

"I have been before, of course, but not for some years, and I should love to pray for peace with the Virgin."

I was becoming self-conscious about my ignorance and resolved to ask Helena to accompany me to mass on Sunday, if she wouldn't mind, so she could whisper instructions to me during the service. Meanwhile, I agreed the rent with Mrs Lisowski, and explained that I would not be able to pay the first month until I had started my new job but could give her a small deposit from what I still had of Alexandre's money. She waived my notes away.

"Helena told me you would be good for the rent and that you plan to start working at Kozlow's Solicitors next week. She has given me a deposit for you, and I have agreed to return it to her when you pay the first month's rent. You can move in tomorrow, if that suits you. I just have to give the place the once-over before you come, and I will of course need your papers for the lodgers' book. You can't be too careful nowadays, and the Gestapo police are often here checking that I have everything up to date."

I promised to bring her my identity papers the next day, knowing too well that this would be a pre-requisite of moving in. If I was unlucky, my ID number would be checked against my original registration as Miriam Weiner, and all would be over for me and Anna.

The next morning I presented myself for interview at Kozlow and Partners, on Radomska, which was a small and old-fashioned firm. Mr Kozlow had received my resumé from Helena, such as it was, and asked why I hadn't worked for so many years. I explained that I had been looking after young children in Krakow, and then as they grew up, my husband had been moving offices quite a lot, and we hadn't been in one place long enough for me to stay in work. I also told him that I'd been working for the business a lot, which in the early days I had certainly helped with, and explained my understanding of accounting, shorthand and other secretarial duties. He didn't seem perturbed by my lack of legal expertise, and he didn't ask about Otto or what the business was called. I suppose that during war, there is a level of decorum among the educated classes not to ask about one's husband or father or son, in case they have not survived. In Mr Kozlow's case, I think it was simply a lack of interest.

"We are only looking for someone who will work hard and always turn up, Mrs Wojcik. We do not expect specialised knowledge, and we can train you in any legal terminology and phraseology you will need to have. I have your reference from Helena Bartosz here. We have used her firm over the last few years to recruit staff, and have always been very happy with her choices, so that reference stands for a lot. If you want the job, it's yours. Please bring your ID papers with you and you can start on Monday."

We moved into the apartment that afternoon, and I started work the following Monday. Anna was enrolled in the local Catholic school to start on the same day, and for the first time in two years, I felt safe.

Helena had been wonderfully supportive, and though she didn't agree to attend mass with me, she sent Emelia along with Anna and me, and the children whispered throughout the mass, and I followed their lead. Within a couple of weeks, I had the prayers and responses learned by heart, and I began to take communion.

The Apartment was luxurious after Lwow, and we managed to settle in quickly. Every day I cooked our dinner, and we lounged comfortably in our small sitting room. Anna's health started to improve, especially as there was some lunch provided at school, and her whole demeanour improved once she was able to spend more time with girls her age, albeit Catholics. She even brought one or two children home after school to keep her company while I finished my day at work, and they seemed to accept the new girl without any questions about her past.

Within two weeks, everything seemed to be quite stable. I was paid by Mr Kozlow and settled up with Mrs Lisowski for the first month's rent, so that she would pay Helena the deposit. Then I went out and spent a few Reichsmarks on a bouquet for Helena as a thank you for all her help and support. She told me off for spending the money, but it was so little, compared to the huge amount she had done.

I went to early mass every day and was already becoming friendly with other congregants, albeit without giving away much about our lives. Despite the blissful relief of living as a Catholic in a Nazi occupied town, where nobody suspected my Jewish origins, I had to contend with anti-Semitic conversations every day at work and even at church. It was strange to find that as soon as I was assumed to be a Catholic, the true nature of this bigotry was opened up to me. I even had to pretend that I agreed with it, laughing at Jewish jokes or smiling when told that some Jews had been arrested. I don't think I was especially offended on behalf of a religion that I no longer belonged to, but I was truly disgusted that people could shun others who had done nothing to them and could all but support the occupying enemy in the process. It was, of course, not so simple, and Polish Catholics were as scared of the Nazis as were many other subjugated groups, but that they saw their salvation in the demise of others, after what I had seen in Lwow, sickened me.

The old lady from further down Karola Szymanowskiego, who also went to seven o'clock mass, told me that she'd found out that some Jews were hiding in a neighbour's attic. She'd had no qualms about reporting them to the Gestapo officer who hung about at the café on the corner. It seems he was stationed there, every morning, with his newspaper and coffee, and his main job was to listen to gossip and to note down anything suspicious.

"So, I told him to get himself along to number 23, and to ask the lady who lives there to show him around. At the top of the stairs, there's a cupboard, which has a false wall at the back, and apparently there's a staircase up to the attic behind there, and there's a whole family living in her attic. I heard it from my friend who lives next door. They thought they had rats in their roof, and when they were up in the eaves, checking what was causing the noise, they heard whispering, and apparently, they could see the glow of candlelight through a hole in the wall. It didn't take long for them to figure out what was going on. Those bloody Yids! They've got some nerve, hiding out in a good Catholic neighbourhood."

"But what will happen to the lady who has been harbouring them?" I asked.

"Who knows, lovey. She must have known the risks. They've been clearing out the Ghetto, and I suppose some of them sneaked out at night and they must have either forced her to take them in, or maybe she's a Jew too. You never know, do you?"

"But don't you think that the Gestapo will take her away and jail her, or maybe worse?"

"She only got her just deserts, I say. And don't you agree, we have to help them get rid of the Jews from Czestochowa, so that the Nazis will leave us in peace? And besides, what did the Jews ever do for us? Just a bunch of money-grubbing trouble-makers if you ask me. They're dirty, and they don't make any effort to mix in here. I heard that they've got gold and diamonds hidden in those houses in the ghetto. Good riddance, I say!"

While I had to pretend I didn't care about this sort of repugnant bigotry, I was much more concerned when Helena told me that she had been asked for a list of all the people who she has on her books, together with their identity numbers. The Germans were, in their typically thorough way, cross-checking the identity numbers against travel permits and with the registrations on file. If she gave them my number, it would only be a matter of time before I would be discovered as Miriam Weiner.

"I haven't been able to provide them with all my files, Miriam. You understand that my records are not completely up to date, and also, there are a number of documents which were damaged by a small flood I had in the office recently…"

"Helena, I am indebted to you for your discretion and help. I appreciate how big a risk it is not to report me."

"I will let you know if they come back looking for more information. However, I can't hold out on them if they go to Mr Kozlow, and he supplies them with a list of names and ID numbers for people whom I have put forward to him. You are, I presume, always ready to move on quickly?"

"Of course. But I have not felt so safe as this in two years, and I hope I can remain here."

CHAPTER 26

Aden

Cresent Hotel, Aden

28th November 1941

My dear Tomasz and Max,

This is my third letter to you, care of your address in Bloomsbury square, the last I have for you. I'm no longer convinced you are still residing with Mrs Stanmore, since you didn't reply to my last two, though of course you may have replied and posted letters which simply didn't reach me in Budapest or Casablanca.

I imagine that Imperial College is no longer running the metallurgy course, whilst London endures the blitz. It may be no more than rubble now, from what I have heard of the terrible bombing. Have you spent your nights in the London underground stations? They report here that everyone is driven into their cellars and into the tunnels of the railways to escape the bombs. I hope so much for your safety.

And what about you, Max? I trust you are both still living together and that you are well occupied. I assume you managed to finish your studies, and that you passed your matriculation examination. I would hope that you are considering some gainful employment in London, where there is a thriving timber import business. I do of course have many contacts but until I hear what you are doing, it is probably best not to try and advance those opportunities. It would also be likely that their wharfs were bombed during the blitz, as these would be prime targets.

As you can see from the letterhead, I am now in Aden, and have travelled with Olek, Maryla and their two children from Budapest, via Casablanca. I was only able to meet up with Olek three months ago, after having been discharged from the regiment, owing to ill health (nothing to be too concerned about, simply a recurrence of my angina). We were stationed in Budapest, but the regiment was being disbanded, and many of my compatriots were travelling to Scotland under General Kukiel, to form an army in exile to help the British fight Hitler. Apparently, Stalin has released a large number of Polish soldiers from prison, to help fight Hitler, since he decided to attack Moscow. I was advised not to go with them, but to go south to Palestine or somewhere else which is hot and dry, and now that we are together here, I also feel that Olek will need support with looking after Maryla and the children. If you are able to find where the regiment is stationed, there are some very fine men among them and you could do worse than join up yourself, Tomasz. I expect there is an headquarters for the Polish Free Army in Edinburgh. I'm not sure what can be done by our chaps in Scotland, though I understand that the Allies see this as a potential point of invasion from Hitler across the North Sea, but I am sure they need all the help they can get.

Olek is not so well himself, and he has suffered a minor heart attack since we last met. He has aged considerably, and now sleeps a great deal. He was so worried about Maryla and the children, caught as they were between the German and Russian advances, and then living under the Bolsheviks for a year or more, and it seems to have taken all his resources to get this far. Maryla has lost a great deal of weight, and the children were very quiet for some time after they all escaped. It is so saddening to see what a sorry state they are all in, and I do what I can to build them up again.

It has been a torturous journey, full of mishaps and administrative blocks. We have been 'on the run' from the advance of Hitler into Africa, and after a great deal of trouble, not to say expense, in Casablanca, we finally find ourselves in a relatively safe haven, in this British protectorate, where there is a thriving Jewish community. We have been here in Aden for two weeks, awaiting more documents, and tickets which will allow us to travel on to Karachi. I must say that it has been a source of great frustration that I have been unable to reach London to find you both, and of more than frustration to tell you that I am still unable to locate or communicate with your dear mother.

I appreciate that you must be extremely worried about her and little Anna, since they returned to Krakow almost two years ago. Though I have not exchanged letters with Miriam, I have in fact heard about her and Anna, and to my knowledge, they are still OK. Here is what I do know:

Your mother took Anna from Krakow to Naleczow soon after returning home, along with your aunt Ania and uncle Paul and their children, because of the declaration of war, and their obvious fear of being over-run by the Nazis. There she met up with Maryla, Szymon and Aneta, and everyone decided they should travel east, as Hitler advanced across Poland. I gather they settled in Lwow, where your resourceful mother found work in a charity, close to where aunt Ada's mother lives. Nevertheless, from the descriptions of life in Lwow from Maryla, I have to say that I have been very worried about your mother and Anna's experiences under the Russians. Miriam is, as you know, one of the most resourceful people alive, and I am convinced that if anyone can survive this terrible ordeal, she can.

Olek was in Danzig, and through his diplomatic contact, Conrad Brzozowski, who was visiting Lwow regularly, managed to obtain travel visas for Maryla and the children, but was unable to help Miriam. I had already tried to apply for documents for her and Anna, when I thought they were in Krakow but of course I failed. Besides, I have only discovered their whereabouts recently, so it would have been impossible to send anything care of Krakow.

Olek retains his diplomatic papers from the work he did in Bucharest for the Rumanian government many years ago, and surprisingly, he was able to persuade the authorities in Berlin that these still have some validity...

But that is another story. Since Olek and Maryla and I met up, I have of course written many times to the address in Lwow, which Maryla had for Miriam, but to no avail. Your mother must have moved, or else Conrad failed to deliver my letters, because I did not hear back from her. Maryla brought one letter with her from Miriam, which I have beside me. It is now six months old, and I have been unable to reply, since Conrad did not return to Danzig before we left. Olek thinks he may have been arrested in Lwow, where we hear that many politicians and diplomats have been jailed by the NKVD and sent to Siberia. In your mother's letter, she asks after your wellbeing, and sends her love, in case I am able to contact you. She said that Anna was unwell and that they were barely able to find enough to eat. She asks me for money, which I am unable to send her. She tells me that the banks have confiscated our accounts, which I of course knew, and she asks for news of Olek. I am sorry that I have not been able to respond to her questions.

I hear from Olek that Stashek Epstein is in Britain, and it is possible that you could try and find him with the Polish forces there. I'm sure that is a tall order, but Gabriela is still in Krakow, so perhaps he could write to her from England, since their letters would not be subjected to the same scrutiny, and perhaps she can reach Miriam. Such a convoluted process this is to send and receive news!

So, I must say that we are forced to keep moving, and Karachi is not somewhere I would have considered in my wildest dreams as a destination, but here in Aden, one has to take one's chances when they come. While most people seek transportation to the United States of America, it is apparent that all the steamers have been requisitioned for the Atlantic Fleet, and nobody is getting berths any more.

Boys, you know I am not a religious man, but if I were, I would pray for your safety. For now, I have to assume you are in perhaps the last safe haven in Europe. I hold myself responsible for asking your mother to return to Krakow from Paris when she was with you there, and I am unfortunately unable to turn back the clocks and recommend to her that she travel with you to London. As you know, we were very often apart at that time, and it was so very hard to know what was best in those weeks before the declaration of war. I must live with the consequences of my decision, and ask those who still believe in a higher power to pray for your mother and sister's safety.

I so hope this missive reaches you, and that you will be able to write to me: Poste Restante, Karachi.

With much love

Your father.

CHAPTER 27

Absolution

Arkhypenka Street, Lwow

11th May 1941

Otto,

I am writing this letter late at night to give to Maryla for you, before she leaves tomorrow. If it reaches you, you will know that she has managed to travel on her visa to Budapest to meet Olek. I feel sure that if she makes the journey without being arrested and deported, she will meet him, and they will know where to find you. I think that this will be my last letter to you because I do not believe that we can continue to survive here much longer, and because I have made a decision about our marriage.

You should know that the last two years have been like hell on earth for Anna and me, and that the terror we have suffered by being caught in Lwow under Russian occupation has been immeasurable. For now, we are not under threat of arrest by the NKVD, but there is much hatred for Jews among the Ukrainian population, and many believe that Hitler will soon want the rest of Poland for himself. You may know more than I do about what happens to Jews who are rounded up and taken away by the SS. I am told that many are taken into the forests and shot, and many more are taken to labour camps where they are starved.

I hold you responsible for our predicament. Your demand that I should return from Paris to Krakow, rather than staying with Tom and Max in London sealed our fate. I say that simply as a fact, as I have stopped being angry about your decision, Otto. At that time, you may have thought it best for us, and certainly you saw merit in the family being together, and in my protecting Maryla. Perhaps you have carried some guilt over the decision. I know I would have done in your position.

We have been married for twenty-two years and have produced three beautiful children. During those years, you have been unfaithful with more than one woman, and for the last ten or fifteen, I know you and Maryla have been having an affair. You have refused to discuss this, and now we have been apart for almost eighteen months, I'm no longer interested in what you have to say. I am only interested in the safety and protection of our children. But I can't do enough to protect them on my own. Max and Tom are, hopefully, safe in England, and unless the Nazis succeed in defeating the British, perhaps they will survive this terrible war. If you are in touch with them, tell them I love them, and I think of them every day. Anna has been sick for some months with dysentery and has lost a great deal of weight. She isn't able to walk far and has had no schooling since she was twelve. Her days are spent lying in her cot, while I slave in a soup kitchen for twelve hours, serving an endless queue of starving refugees. But that is the reality of this war, and I do what I can for her.

I am writing this letter to give you your absolution from our marriage. If you and Maryla are destined to be together, then take better care of her than you have of me, because she is a good and kind mother who is not as strong as I am. If you are not, then perhaps you will still find someone more suited to you to spend your days with.

Whatever your future holds, please do not desert your children in the way you have deserted me. They don't deserve that, and they don't understand you as I do.

I wish you well.

Miriam.

CHAPTER 28

Flight

I knew that the false papers would only work for us until the efficient German bureaucracy asked Kozlow for his register of employees and reverted to the main register to check all the ID numbers. It would be a matter of time, and I would have to be ready to pull Anna out of school and to flee without time to spare. I always kept a packed overnight bag in our lodgings, and I carried our papers with me at all times, in the hope that we would still be able to use them if we could be forewarned of discovery.

Helena knew someone in the Jewish Fighting Organisation, an underground movement in the ghetto, who was in touch with a secretary or clerk working in the SS headquarters. Apparently, this clerk was a Catholic woman who had married a Jew who had been taken away and shot. She had been intercepting and disseminating SS communications pertaining to investigations of Jews in Czestochowa.

Helena agreed to warn me if my name appeared in Gestapo lists of suspected Jews living in the city, and it transpired that I was not the only Jewish employee on her books. It was precious little insurance, but certainly more than I had hoped for before coming to Czestochowa.

The job was reasonable, though I didn't warm to most of my colleagues, who were remarkably indifferent to the Nazis' treatment of Jews from the ghetto. They would laugh and joke about arrests and even describe the beatings they'd witnessed in the streets with some glee.

One morning, in the office, I received a note from the delivery boy who brought parcels, and he slipped it surreptitiously into my hand as I signed for the day's parcel delivery. It was from Helena, who told me I had to get out immediately as my false name had come up on a list, alongside my place of work, as a suspected Jew. It wasn't clear whether Mr Kozlow had been required to submit the papers of all his staff to the Gestapo, but that was probably the cause of the discovery, rather than my train ticket. It also wasn't clear whether he had been notified of my status. I thought it unlikely since the SS would want an element of surprise in all arrests, and they would not need to notify anyone of their plans.

I went to see Mr Kozlow immediately. He was a quiet, older man who had kept his views to himself about the Germans since I'd known him. When his business partner once laughed and joked to everyone in the office about how he had reported some Jews to the Gestapo who were in hiding in his neighbour's garage, under his truck in the oil pit, and how they'd been rounded up and deported, Mr Kozlow did not participate. He grimaced and retreated into his office.

"I'm sorry to bother you sir, but would you mind if I took an early lunch today? My daughter is sick and I must collect her medication from the pharmacy."

"No problem, Mrs Wojcik, but be back in an hour." He smiled at me, and I knew in that moment that he had no inkling of what might happen.

I collected my handbag, and left the office, as if to go for lunch. I rushed to the school and collected Anna from her class, claiming to the teacher that I had had an urgent message regarding her grandmother's heart attack. Anna already knew that this meant we had to leave immediately and to go along with the story. We ran back to Karola Szymanowskiego and let ourselves into the house. Luckily, the landlady was out, so we grabbed our few belongings together and walked to Czestochowa station, trying not to look scared or to run. We passed many soldiers gathered on street corners or lounging outside cafes, and each time I wondered if we had been under surveillance and would be stopped to have our papers checked. However efficient the Gestapo system, I thought it unlikely that soldiers on street corners would already have a list of ID numbers against which to check everyone's papers, but I could be wrong.

At the station, there was a queue for tickets, and of course, a soldier checking papers next to the ticket booth. We had no choice but to brazen it out and hope that the list of names had not been circulated yet. Luckily, he was simply looking at photographs and names, and didn't have anything to cross-check ID numbers against. Within the hour, we were on the first train leaving, and had tickets for Krosno, a small town towards the Slovakian border, a backwater I felt we could hide in. I had often checked the various direct train routes out of Czestochowa, but in truth, if the next train had been to Krakow or Lublin, we might have taken it.

When we arrived in Krosno, we found out that the ghetto had already been emptied and many of the Jews taken to Rzeszów, a labour camp from which nobody escaped. Our papers were checked three times in our first hour in the town, and passed inspection, so we were again looking for accommodation and work for me, and schooling for Anna, but this time without the help of Helena, who had been such a support for the last few months. I had managed to save some Reichsmarks while working for Kozlow, so this time it was easier to use money in order to secure our futures.

Again I managed to rent a room for us, though it was not nearly as comfortable as our last lodgings, and after a few weeks, I found work as a secretary, in a small clothing factory. This time, I was the only administrator, responsible for all paperwork, and so I was lucky enough to be in charge of personnel records. I was able to make sure that my ID number didn't appear on the register of employees, and nobody else in the company ever checked these. We had regular checks from the town hall, which was overseen by German administrators, but because Kosno was so much smaller, and clearly not a strategic location at all, they sent a local employee to collect the register, and he was not diligent.

I was able to enroll Anna into the local Catholic school, and Anna's ID number, which we were obliged to present at the school, was much less likely to be checked.

Soon, we were integrating with local church-goers and our neighbours and avoiding any activities or conversations which might expose us to capture.

We lived in Kosno for almost three years, until early 1946, when I could return to Krakow as the Soviets drove out the German forces. The time passed slowly, and we had little news of the progress of the war. Anna recovered somewhat from her dysentery, though she never returned to full health. All I could say about myself is that I survived.

CHAPTER 29

Mussourie

The valley swept away below the house. Otto sat, reading in the late afternoon sun, dressed in his corduroy trousers, and wearing a cardigan, despite the clear blue skies, with a rug draped loosely over his knees. His hair had turned white, and his moustache was unkempt. Maryla was always trying to trim it for him, as she had done when they first met, but he objected to her interference, while not bothering to look after it himself. He liked to chew the ends while reading.

Two spotted eagles circled high above the garden, riding the updrafts, searching for mice and rats in the fields, and crickets chirped in the rhododendron bushes. Sanjay was pruning the roses on the lower terrace, and Savita swept the veranda, but otherwise, there was silence and stillness.

Otto had been reading MC's editorial in the National Herald about the inevitability of partition since the war had ended. He wondered how long it would take for the British to relinquish control in Lucknow. He put the paper down on the small teak side-table and looked across the hills towards Mussoorie. He could smell the peach blossom and wondered how he'd ignored this wonderful fragrance for so many years.

The sun felt warm on his bare arms, but the air was fresh, and it was only in the last few weeks that the Himalayan winds had begun to warm. He thought about November in Krakow, and the fur coat he would need, had he been sitting outside at this time there. He had a fleeting image of himself and Olek outside Café Zentral, in the Kazimierz, indulging in a plate of knedle while they talked through their day's business, their breath in white clouds, their coffees cooling all too rapidly. That was less than ten years ago, but it seemed a lifetime. Poor Olek. They'd buried him in Karachi after that second heart attack had taken him. He'd been Olek's business partner for ten years, and travelling companion for two, from Hungary to Casablanca, then Aden and on to Pakistan. They'd been through so much together, and shared everything, even Maryla. When Olek was in the hospital, in that plain white room with its tiled walls, on his last day, they'd had a few words.

"Take care of our loved ones. I know you will," Olek whispered.

"Listen, my friend. You'll be up and about again very soon, and we need you to get your strength up. We must find somewhere out of this interminable heat for you to rest up. We'll go into the mountains. It'll be like Zakopane. Remember those trips?"

"No Otto. My skiing days are over. This is it. I won't be travelling on with you all. But I want you to know I never blamed you for how things turned out."

"Please, let's not talk this way."

"For Maryla. The children. She loves you, and we've made our peace about that, she and I."

Otto thought of writing again to Tomasz in London, but he had had no reply to his previous letters, which he assumed had gone astray, or that Tom had moved digs. It was of course ridiculous to hope that the post would follow a student from room to room across that great city, if it had even reached London. He'd long since given up writing to Miriam in Krakow. It had been four years since he'd had any word of her whereabouts, and the chances were that post wasn't even getting through now, since the communists had taken over in Warsaw and there was reportedly no order in Krakow. But even if it were, he had no idea whether she had survived. Only now was it becoming clear what had happened, what had been done by the Nazis and the Russians to his country.

He thought about the last time he'd seen Miriam, in Vichy. How they'd fought about Maryla, and his returning to Danzig when she needed him to pay attention to his family. How he had hated her then. How that had faded, along with the sound of her shrill abuse. He pulled her photo from his wallet. It had been taken in '36, in Vienna. He closed his eyes, heard the Strauss waltz, the clinking of fine china and the hum of voices in the restaurant.

When Maryla returned to the house, after collecting Aneta from school, she ordered tea to be brought out to the veranda. As she came over to wake Otto, she noticed his mouth had dropped open and his head hung at an odd angle. He wasn't breathing.

Mussoorie, March 19th 1946

My darling,

It's so lonely, now you've gone. I felt I had to find some way to communicate with you. Each day I visit your grave and talk, but today I wanted to write to you. I'm sitting under the shade of the bougainvillea, which is in flower, and Sanjiv is busy on the lower terrace, pruning the roses. The air is fresh and there's a light breeze. You'd love to be sitting beside me here; I know you would. Our spotted eagles are circling over the mountain, as always, and the crickets are chirping. It is so peaceful.

I had a shock this morning, when a letter came for you. Just seeing your name brought tears to my eyes, and then to realize from all the postmarks and crossed out addresses that it was from Krakow via London. It had to be from Tomasz or Miriam. I sat with it for a long time before deciding to open it. Finally, with trepidation for the bad news I expected, I opened it and it was from Miriam. After all these years, and too late for you, it felt so precious. It was in her precise handwriting, which I remembered from so long ago, and it was very moving. She's alive and well, and living with Tomasz and Max, who managed to bring her to England from Poland. She didn't say much about the last five years, but I could tell it was awful. You would be so happy to know that Anna is also with them. They all survived!

Miriam tells you that Anna has never recovered from her dysentery, having spent years in terrible conditions with poor nutrition, but there are many good people helping them in London, and your boys are both in fine shape.

Oh Otto. I'm so sorry you aren't here to read such wonderful news, and to be able to reply. You spent so long feeling guilty and fearful that they didn't make it, and now I am the one who must write back to her. I hardly know where to begin. I can't hide the facts, and I can't lie to her. Since poor Olek's death, it will be obvious to her that we've lived as man and wife, since she knew about us long ago, but what do I tell her about the children? Surely she must have known. I know she had her suspicions when they were born, but in all our months together in Lwow, she never once raised them with me. She was so gracious and strong and helpful to us. I know we talked about this so many times, but now you're not here to help me, I feel overwhelmed with the responsibility. I think it's too much for anyone to manage, and especially after what Miriam has been through. It's as much as I can do to tell her of your death, and how we spent your last years together, after Olek. I can't also tell her about the children.

I will do my best to write well. I will tell her how you suffered for not being able to reach her, and how hard you found it to leave her behind. I will send her details of how to find your last resting place, should she ever manage to make the journey here to Mussoorie. But I just can't tell her outright about Szymon and Aneta – I am afraid I am too weak to do that.

I went into the travel agents in Lucknow yesterday, when Aneta was in school, and I have made reservations for us all on a sailing to New York next month. It will be so hard to leave here, and to sail into the unknown. As we agreed last year, I'm going to try and buy a place that is suitable for a boarding house. Szymon is old enough to be man of the house, and Aneta can earn pocket money by helping me with meals and cleaning. I so wish you were coming with us, but I will always remember our happy time here.

I wanted to tell you something, which I should have told you when I could have heard your reply. I don't know what kept me from saying it, but perhaps it was because we'd spent so many years without being open, and I knew how much of a burden it was for you not knowing what had happened to Miriam and your children.

When Olek was in the hospital, that day after his heart attack, he said very little. I told you then that his only words were that he loved me, and that was all. He was very weak, and I had only moments with him when he was conscious, but he said more than that. He told me that he forgave us and asked me to care for you as the father of his children, and that he loved you as his brother. Now you're gone, I feel lost. I should have told you, and I know you would have been happy to hear it.

I must say goodbye for now my darling. I will visit you every day until we leave here.

Your Maryla.

CHAPTER 30

Kilburn 1972

There were always fine threads and hairs on the carpet. Miriam couldn't understand where they were coming from. However meticulously she picked each one up, there always seemed to be more. It didn't make sense. She didn't have pets, and she was living alone, but every day it was the same. The grey wool carpet showed up every particle of dust, and those hairs. Max had bought her a Hoover, but she preferred to use a carpet brush and her fingers. You just couldn't get the Hoover to pick up each and every one, and it was important not to miss any. When the sun shone through the lounge windows she could see hairs and dust particles floating in the light.

It felt ridiculous that she should be reduced to spending her days cleaning up, but there really was no choice. Every day the kitchen floor needed washing, and she did it because she was alone, though she really felt too old to be on her hands and knees. It was not supposed to be this way.

She was sitting in the lounge bay window, overlooking the communal waste bins and patch of scruffy lawn behind the mansion block. She was polishing the silver cake forks from her treasured cutlery service, the one Celestyna had dug up and rescued from her sister's garden in '46, and presented to Miriam with great ceremony, along with the Meissen teapot, which was sadly cracked and useless. That was before Tomasz took her with him to London to live, and to Fordwych Court, and this apartment in Kilburn, which he and Max had rented for her. Each piece of cutlery needed a great deal of care, and the walnut cutlery cabinet, which had been wrapped in a tarpaulin for six years, was wax polished every day.

Hardly a blemish on the cabinet, and the silver was as good as new, after its tarnish had been removed. She'd dusted the Chinese vases, eighteenth century blue and white, on the sideboard, and the Meissen teapot. The glue holding the china together was yellow now, but they were still beautiful. They would of course have been hugely valuable, had they not all been chipped and cracked when they were finally shipped after the war.

'One has to take care of one's few possessions. I learned that in Lwow, hiding my jewelry in the chimney in that cold garret, once we'd run out of fuel to burn. To think, I had two maids, a housekeeper, a cook and a driver at one time, and accounts at all the great department stores in Vienna.'

Miriam moved the bucket and wrung out the cloth once again, as she scrubbed the clean lino for a second time.

'Tomasz and Max are such good boys for visiting their mother, and helping with the rent, but it is still hard to be alone. But we all have our own cross to bear. Poor Anna, with her seaweed remedies and herbal teas; it hasn't been easy for her either. She told me recently that she has to sleep alone in a child's bed, with her nose against the wall, curled into a ball.'

Polishing the silver always brought back memories of Alexandre, in his restaurant in Vienna in the twenties. She could see the chandeliers sparkling as though it was yesterday, and almost hear the waltzes, but her memories of him were cast in shadow. She only had the one photograph of him. In it, he was standing alone, in a civilian suit with that high-waisted pants 1930s cut. He was in front of some poor stone cottages, on a dirt road, holding a guidebook.

'What a shame I don't have one of him in his red hussar's jacket and epaulettes, and that manicured moustache he wore in the twenties. I loved how he looked, so dashing and strong.'

Miriam sat upright on the edge of the sofa-bed, working Silvo into the blade of a cake knife whose swirling engraved design tended to harbour tarnish. She was dressed in an aging French navy tweed skirt and cashmere cardigan, even though the flat was overly warm, and her reading glasses hung from a fine gilt chain around her neck, over the pearls she always wore.

'How splendid I looked that first evening in the Café Austerlitz, in that beautiful blue silk dress and my diamonds, or was it that wondrous cream taffeta with the pearls? Alexandre. Where are you now? Are you in your own little heaven, a place for Nazis who refused to do as they were told? Did you meet your end in a firing squad, or perhaps you slipped away to South America, like they say so many did?'

Would it have ended differently if she'd accepted his offer to move to Vienna before the war?

'But I had the children, a home to take care of. And besides, how would we have hidden our differences when the Nazis came to power? Our paths took two completely different directions, and there was no going back to find one another. Perhaps he did survive. He was well connected, well-travelled. He could have acquired false papers and managed to escape. Imagine. He could have pretended to be a Jew!'

Whenever Miriam scrubbed the floor in her little kitchen, with a pail of water and her old housecoat on, it brought back the stink of carbolic from that attic. 'How hard I tried to keep some semblance of order, some sort of self-respect. Oh, and those cat hairs which were impossible to get rid of. Anna, poor child. Allergic to cats, and I could do nothing, but pick them up all the time.'

When she walked past the small French restaurant on Kilburn Highroad, and the smells of cooking wafted from the door, she always thought of the Café Austerlitz, where his chefs prepared her favourite Wiener Schnitzel, and the delightful French waiters in their long white aprons carried huge silver trays of drinks and steaming food on their shoulders between the busy tables.

'Anna and Jan brought borscht round for dinner yesterday, and some of the babcia rye bread, which I love. I wish she wouldn't let him cook though. He's a good man but I worry about his level of hygiene. He spends his days making pots, and then he prepares dinner. Anna brought her special seaweed concoction in a small plastic tub. The poor girl never regained her appetite after Lwow. It was hard for her, finding a husband after everything, and though I would have preferred to see her marry an educated man, someone we knew, Jan is a good man and cares for her. If her father had lived, he would have stopped their marriage. But the old ways seem to have been forgotten.

Acknowledgement

Thanks to the work of my father, George, for his genealogical research in the 1990s, which led to the discovery of his two siblings in the US, my uncle Stephen and aunt Anita. His photos, descriptions and translations of correspondence and other notes written by my grandmother during and after the war have given me much of the raw material for the book.

Thanks also to Mary Morrissy, who helped me so much with my writing, as my tutor on the UCC MA, and who edited many iterations of the short stories, 'Miriam' and 'Otto' which preceded this novel.

Thanks too to Meabh, Noel, Beca and Paul who read for me and to Val who had to contend with my process of writing

While the bones of this story are true, and the wartime historical context has been researched as thoroughly as possible, this is a novel and all its characters are fictional. With the death of my father and his siblings, the truth about Miriam and Otto's lives is buried.

Adrian Wistreich